# Introducing MAP
# in
# Industrial Communications
# Networks

## Colin Pye

NCC Blackwell
MANCHESTER • OXFORD

British Library Cataloguing in Publication Data

Pye, Colin
  Introducing MAP in Industrial Communications networks.
  1. Business firms.   Electronic communications systems.
  I. Title
  651.7

  ISBN 0-85012-640-1

*MARGARET*

*AND*

*CHARLOTTE*

Published for NCC Publications by NCC Blackwell.

Editorial Office: The National Computing Centre Limited, Oxford Road,
Manchester M1 7ED, England.

NCC Blackwell, 108 Cowley Road, Oxford OX4 1JF, England.

Typeset in 10pt Times Roman by H&H Graphics, Blackburn; and printed by
Hobbs the Printers of Southampton.

ISBN 0-85012-640-1

D
621.78
PYE

# Contents

# Introduction

This book takes a more detailed look at MAP and is based upon the MAP version 3.0 specification. The structure of the book is such that it will take the reader through a number of distinct stages which are intended to flow logically. The objective of the book is to provide enough information to allow the reader to understand the MAP origins and scope, to get a feel for the products available and to recognise how to access MAP in order to fit it into their own environment, given the previous two points. The book is not meant to be a substitute for either the MAP specification or product literature from the suppliers. It is meant to provide a concise overview for the uninitiated. It is essential that any company seriously contemplating using MAP should join a MAP User Group and develop close relationships with the various suppliers. MAP will not solve all of the problems of manufacturing industry – realistically one could not expect it to do so. What MAP could do within an organisation is to help with the rationalisation process.

MAP is a specification which defines the use of international standards. It was conceived by General Motors in the United States and grew out of the need to enable incompatible equipment, installed on the factory floor, to communicate cost effectively. General Motors has put much time and effort into MAP – their contribution to the acceptance of MAP in particular and OSI in general should be duly acknowledged. The task was not a simple one and their (and other organisations') efforts are now coming to fruition.

Since MAP is based on International Standards the book assumes some knowledge of Open System Interconnection (OSI). Chapter 1 does give a brief overview of the International Standards Organisation's (ISO) reference model for Open Systems Interconnection. For readers requiring more background they are directed towards the NCC publication *What is OSI?*.

7

The book does not deal with the cost justification of adopting MAP because if 'N' different companies are considered there will be 'N' different communication network designs leading to 'N' different views on cost justification. MAP must be thought through in relation to the organisation's Computer Integrated Manufacturing (CIM) strategy. This book does not address CIM specifically but it must be understood that manufacturing efficiency encompasses not just the manufacturing process but invoicing, stock control and despatch in addition to other related support areas. Essentially it is the control of *information* from market research, design, development, manufacture, marketing and sales – a daunting task. Each of the functions has a different set of requirements associated with it and consequently a different set of technical solutions – the key is in *integrating*. MAP has evolved in such a way that it recognises this need and is now moving towards it. It is the integration of these areas, encompassing the use of the voice and data and globally termed 'Information Technology' strategies which should be considered by the intended user.

Chapter 2 describes the MAP architecture while Chapter 3 describes key areas of the MAP specification, broadly based on Version 3. Following the objective of the book, Chapter 4 describes some of the products and systems currently available. This Chapter, although only a snapshot, provides the basis on which to illustrate some of the teaching points worthy of note.

Chapter 5 describes how to assess the role of MAP within your organisation; and Chapter 6 describes the key to advancing MAP. The user obviously needs that 'warm feeling' that MAP is here to stay.

In essence then the book is essentially split into two parts:

**Part 1: MAP – The Theory** comprises Chapters 1, 2 and 3, while

**Part 2: MAP – The Practice** comprises Chapters 4, 5 and 6.

The Appendix comprises a glossary of well-used terms.

# Part 1

# MAP --- The Theory

# 1 The ISO Architectural Model

## 1.1 INTRODUCTION

This chapter explains the role of the International Standards Organisation's architectural model.

Architectural concepts and layering are fundamental to systems design. It is clear that some sort of structure must be created, when designing a system, in order to facilitate its interconnection to other systems. Fundamental to this process is defining the functionality of the system's constituent parts. The International Standards Organisation's reference model for Open Systems Interconnection is not a network architecture but defines a framework into which the services and functionality of a system may be placed. The openness of a system is not meant to imply the use of any particular technology or specific means of interconnection. It is meant to define the standardised means of recognising the information transferred between systems, as opposed to the internal designs of the systems themselves.

MAP is based on OSI and so it is important to understand the basic concept of OSI. In later chapters we see how MAP applies the concept of OSI in order to fulfil the requirements demanded of it.

ISO is interested in defining globally accepted international standards. The ISO's reference model for OSI is one such base standard. It defines the framework within which other standards may operate. It is impossible to say that one particular design for the architectural make-up of a system is the best, but ordering of the functions within each layer is necessary, and is based on a consensus. The 'openness' of a system, as previously described, is not meant to imply the use of any particular technology or specific means to interconnection. It is meant to define the standardised means of recognising the information transferred between systems, as opposed to the internal designs of the systems

11

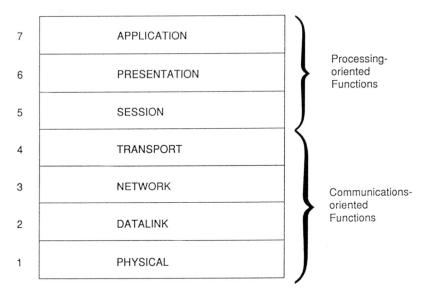

**Figure 1.1   The ISO 7-Layer Reference Model**

themselves. With this in mind we can now look at the ISO reference model and consider some of the terms used within it. These are intended to make the framework structure (around which a system may be designed) more easily understandable in terms of the functions and services it is meant to provide.

**The Reference Model**

The ISO has defined a seven-layer reference model for OSI (Figure 1.1). The OSI reference model achieves the objective of interconnection of open systems by describing an ordered structure of subsystems (Figure 1.2).

Figure 1.2 illustrates the relationship between any layer N, its next highest layer N + 1, and the next lowest layer N – 1. Each subsystem provides services to a subsystem of higher rank by means of entities in the subsystem. As described above, the (N)-layer must provide services to the (N+1)-layer. However, an N entity may need to combine with another N entity (in a different system) in order to perform a certain function. To do this it must use the services of the layer immediately below it – the (N–1)-layer. Figure 1.3 illustrates the relationship between layers, services, entities and communication. The communication is carried out by adhering to a protocol for that particular layer – the (N)-protocol.

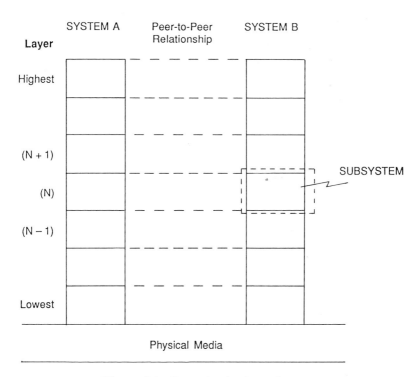

**Figure 1.2   Layering in Open Systems**

An N entity may communicate with an N – 1 entity in order to request an N – 1 service, but to do this it requires a specifically defined interface. The reference model details how N entities and N – 1 entities may connect to N – 1 services access points (interfaces) and how they can exchange information across the interface. (The reader is directed to the ISO standards for more information.)

The N + 1 entity requests the service of an N entity through an N service access point. In turn, The N entity may require to communicate with a peer entity using an N – 1 connection. The information exchanged in this transfer consists predominantly of two parts:

— The N service data unit, comprising the data the N entities required to perform the functions for the service required by the N + 1 entity;

— The N protocol information – the information required to co-ordinate the operation of the exchange between the N entities.

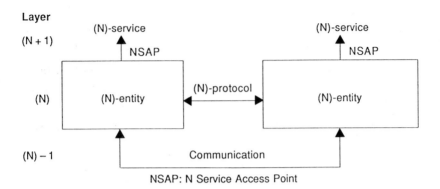

**Figure 1.3   Layer Entities**

The combination of the N service data unit and the N protocol control information is called an N protocol data unit. N entities wishing to communicate must request the service of an N − 1 connection between them. To do this, communication is achieved by an N − 1 service access point to which the N entity attaches. The information which is passed comprises:

— the N − 1 interface control information, which is used to co-ordinate N and N − 1 entities;

— the N − 1 interface data, which normally contains the N protocol data unit (as described previously).

The total information passed between the two layers is called the N − 1 interface data unit.

The process of exchanging data units between the layers is repeated for every layer. There are, however, two exceptions:

— the highest layer, where there is no N + 1 entity as such;

— the lowest layer, where there is no N − 1 entity as such.

In each layer two types of service data unit are defined, the normal N service data unit and the expedited N service data unit. It is worthwhile mentioning these, as things are not quite as they seem in terms of the expedited N service data unit. The expedited N service data unit is not a priority service as such. Its definition means that it *may* be delivered across a connection before normal N service data units, even when those N service data units were submitted earlier. However, it is *guaranteed* that the expedited N service data unit will not be delivered after normal N service data units which were submitted later.

Now that terms such as entities, services and connections have been introduced it can be seen that the reference model adheres to a structured and formalised approach. The main points to remember are that:

— each layer may communicate only with the layers immediately above and immediately below;

— the communication which takes place across the boundary is done in a formalised way by means of what can be thought of as 'sockets' at each layer's interface.

Bear these points in mind when reading the rest of this chapter, and be aware that there is data and control information, and an addressing structure defining the mapping of services and access points at each layer.

The reference model as defined by the ISO contains seven layers (illustrated in Figure 1.1):

— the application layer (layer 7);

— the presentation layer (layer 6);

— the session layer (layer 5);

— the transport layer (layer 4);

— the network layer (layer 3);

— the data link layer (layer 2);

— the physical layer (layer 1);

The application layer consists of application entities which co-operate in the OSI environment. The lower layers, under the application layer, provide the services through which the application entities co-operate. Layers 1-6 (physical to presentation) provide a step by step enhancement of the communication services; the boundary between adjacent layers identifies a stage in this enhancement of services at which an OSI service standard is defined. The functioning of the layers is governed by the OSI protocol standards.

We are now in a position to look at the service and functionality provided by each of these layers, starting with layer 1 – the physical layer.

## 1.2   THE PHYSICAL LAYER

This is the layer responsible for the transparent transmission of information across the physical medium. The layer contains all the functions required to satisfy this condition. Point-to-point or multipoint configurations are defined for the physical connection. When multiple endpoints of the physical connection are present, in the multipoint definition, the physical layer must provide the data link entities with a means to identify the endpoint where a corresponding data link entity is attached. The information transmitted over the physical media, in terms of a bit serial or 'N' bit parallel, must be delivered in the same order in which it was offered for transmission by the data link entity. The overall physical connection can be operated in the full duplex mode or in the half duplex mode.

It is entirely feasible for various data circuits to go into the making of a physical connection, as in the circuit switching concept of the voice network. Once the circuit switches have been made, the physical connection behaves as a single transmission medium. None of the layers above the physical layer are aware of the transmission media making the overall connection, so the overall connection could comprise copper cable, fibre optics, free space, etc, in any combination.

The basic specification in the physical layer can be split into four areas:

— electrical;

— mechanical;

— functional;

— procedural.

The electrical specification defines such things as voltage levels, etc; the mechanical specification defines allocations of pins, dimensions of plugs, etc; the functional specification defines such things as the meaning of voltage levels on certain wires, etc; while the procedural specification defines the rules applying to various functions, sequences in which events may occur, etc. It is not proposed to discuss the individual standards within this book; however, the reader is directed towards them for further reference.

Figure 1.4 illustrates how a physical connection may be provided by the interconnection of data circuits using a relay at the physical layer. It also serves to illustrate the fact that the physical medium itself is not strictly part of the physical layer. Figure 1.5 and 1.6 show the relationship between point-to-point

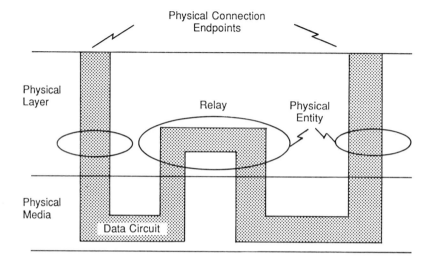

**Figure 1.4   Data Circuit Interconnection**

and multipoint connections, demonstrating in the latter case multi-endpoint physical connections.

The services provided by the physical layer and the functions in the physical layer can thus be summarised as follows:

Services

— physical connections;

— physical service data units;

— physical connection endpoints;

— data circuit identification;

— sequencing;

— fault condition notification;

— quality of service parameters.

Functions

— physical connection activation and deactivation;

— physical service data unit transmission;

— physical layer management.

The layer immediately above the physical layer is the data link layer.

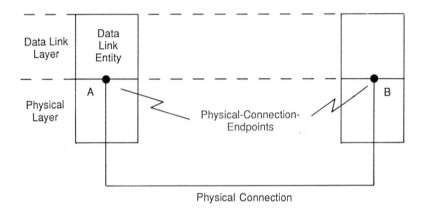

**Figure 1.5   Two-endpoint Physical Connection**

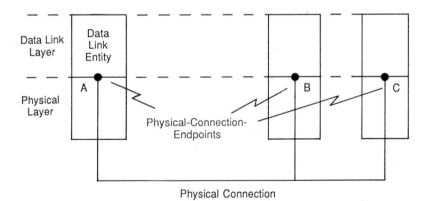

**Figure 1.6   Multi-endpoint Physical Connection**

## 1.3 THE DATA LINK LAYER

The main function of the data link layer is to shield the higher layers from the characteristics of the physical transmission medium. In order to do this it provides the higher layers with a reliable transmission which is basically error free. It should be recognised that errors can and will occur in the actual transmission on the physical connection, and thus it is the responsibility of the data link layer to provide error detection (and, if possible, error correction) in a way that is independent of the data being transmitted. The data link connection, built on top of one or more physical connections, connects two network entities in adjacent systems. The data link layer itself does not provide either segmenting or blocking (see Glossary). Each service data unit from the network entity is mapped on a one-to-one basis into a data link protocol data unit together with the data link protocol information. This data link protocol data unit is called a frame.

As described previously, the physical layer is only concerned with information as a string of bits and it is the responsibility of the data link layer to identify the start and end of this bit stream so it can recognise the information being transmitted. This then allows it to recognise the beginning and end of a frame. It can be likened to putting punctuation marks into a page of text, thus making it more easily understood.

Error detection, and possibly correction, are an inherent part of the data link layer. Error correction can be achieved through retransmission, but this implies that some sequencing information on a transmitted frame is kept; if retransmission is required this will allow the frames to be accepted in the same order as they were transmitted. This is particularly important because the frames received across the data link must be handed over to the network entity in the same sequence in which they were offered for transmission.

Flow control mechanisms can be defined for the data link connection. This means that a data link entity can request a corresponding data link entity to temporarily stop the transmission of frames.

The services provided by and the functions in the data link layer can thus be summarised as follows:

Services

—  data link connections;

—  data link service data units;

— data link connection endpoint indentifiers;

— sequencing;

— error notification;

— flow control;

— quality of service parameters.

Functions

— data link connection establishment and release;

— data link service data units mapping;

— data link connection splitting;

— delimiting and synchronisation;

— sequence control;

— error detection;

— error recovery;

— flow control;

— identification and parameter exchange;

— control of data circuit interconnection;

— data link layer management.

The management within each individual layer would be correlated to the overall management function described in Section 1.9.

The next layer to consider, the one immediately above the data link layer, is the network layer.

## 1.4   THE NETWORK LAYER

The network layer provides the transparent transfer of all data submitted by the transport layer to any transport entity anywhere in the open systems environment. In this way the transport layer has no need to know about the way in which the communicating systems are interconnected; the network connection may therefore be between two open systems ( on a point-to-point basis) or between many open systems. If many open systems are involved the transport entity need not necessarily be adjacent, which means that the network layer must provide routeing functions. Each node (or intermediate system) within a network performs a relay function along the chosen route in order to pass the message on to the next node. Each intermediate system may be a network in itself, and the reference model allows for this. A practical example would be the interconnection of public networks, private networks and local area networks. Network addresses are used to identify transport entities to the network layer. The network layer provides network connections between pairs of network addresses, meaning there is no possibility for multipoint network connections.

The actual routeing strategies are not defined in the reference model. What is defined is that the network layer may or may not maintain the sequence of the data handled for the transport layer. This has to do with the fact that certain routeing schemes inherently maintain the sequence, while others cannot guarantee it. The transport layer must, however, be made aware of the service provided when the network connection is established. This will then allow the transport layer, if necessary, to augment that service to the level required by the session entities.

In some cases an overall connection is made using sub-networks. A sub-network is defined as a set of one or more intermediate systems which provide relaying, and through which end systems may establish network connections. Care must be taken with the overall quality of the network connection. This can best be illustrated considering Figures 1.7 and 1.8. In Figure 1.7 the quality of the resulting network connection cannot be higher than that of the lower quality sub-network. In Figure 1.8 the lower quality sub-network is enhanced to be equal to the higher quality sub-network, and the sub-networks are then interconnected. The resultant quality of the network connection is approximately that of the higher quality sub-network. Because each end of a sub-network connection may operate with a different sub-network protocol, it is clear that care needs

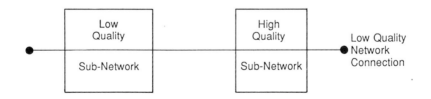

*Overall connection is only as good as the lowest quality connection*

**Figure 1.7    Low Quality and High Quality Sub-network Interconnection**

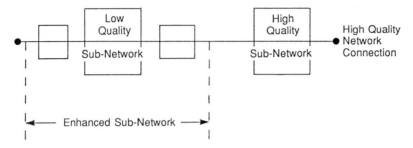

*Overall connection is as good as the high quality sub-network*

**Figure 1.8    Enhanced Low Quality and High Quality Sub-network Interconnection**

to be taken when defining network connections and relating them to the sub-network connections.

The services provided by, and the functions in, the network layer can thus be summarised as follows:

Services

— network addresses;

— network connections;

— network connection endpoint identifiers;

— network service data unit transfer;

— quality of service parameters;

— error notification;

— sequencing;

— flow control;

— expedited network service data unit transfer;

— reset;

— release services.

Functions

— routeing and relaying;

— network connections;

— network connection multiplexing;

— segmenting and blocking;

— error detection;

— error recovery;

— sequencing;

— flow control;

— expedited data transfer;

— reset;

— service selection;

— network layer management.

As mentioned earlier, the network layer provides the transparent transfer of all data submitted by the transport layer, this being the layer immediately above the network layer.

## 1.5   THE TRANSPORT LAYER

A transport connection is provided to the session entities (see Section 1.6, The Session Layer). This is independent of their location, as the transport layer is responsible for the transparent transfer of data between these entities. The transport layer must optimise the use of the communication resources available to it to connect systems together and must also maintain a guaranteed quality of service. The session entity may request a certain quality of service, and once this has been provided by the transport layer it must be maintained. If a case arose in which the transport layer could not maintain the quality of service it would be obliged to notify the session entities of the fact immediately. The transport layer is not aware of the structure of the underlying layers, nor of the topology of the network which provides the access to the physical medium. It is only concerned with the transfer of data between session entities; so all transport protocols have end-to-end significance. This means that the transport layer is not concerned with the network on a step-by-step basis. However, depending on the quality of the network connection the transport layer may have to perform additional functions in order to offer the agreed quality of service.

The transport layer provides users of the transport service (each uniquely identified by a transport address) with transport connections between these addresses. These connections are full duplex (two-way simultaneous). Multipoint transport connections are not defined in the current reference model.

It is possible to arrange for more than one transport connection between the same pair of transport addresses. These are identifiable to transport users through a transport connection endpoint identifier, uniquely defined for each transport connection endpoint. When the transport connection is established, the transport user can request a certain class of service which is a predefined set of service parameters, and which allows the transport layer to allocate resources based on the class of service requirements. Figure 1.9 illustrates the classes of transport service.

```
Class 0 : Simple Class, no enhancement to the network service
Class 1 : Basic Error Recovery Class
Class 2 : Multiplexing Class
Class 3 : Error Recovery and Multiplexing Class
Class 4 : Error Detection and Recovery Class
```

**Figure 1.9    Classes of Transport Service**

As mentioned earlier, the transport layer must achieve optimisation of the connection, and to do this it may use multiplexing (mapping several transport connections onto one network connection) or splitting (mapping one transport connection onto several network connections). In addition ( in order to avoid network congestion caused by session entities over-running each other) the transport layer must perform control. Optionally it may use segmenting and blocking to fit in with the characteristics of the network's connections, or to use them more efficiently.

A summary of the services provided by and the functions in the transport layer is as follows:

Services

Identification:

— transport addresses;

— transport connections;

— transport connection endpoint identifiers.

Establishment Services:

— transport connection establishment;

— class of service selection.

Data Transfer Services

— transport service data unit;

— expedited transport services data unit.

Phases of Operation

Establishment Phase:

— obtain network connection (matching requirements of session entity and taking into account cost and quality of services);

— multiplexing or splitting;

— optimum transport protocol data units size;

— select functions that will be operational during data phase;

— map transport address onto network addresses;

— provide identification of different transport connections between the same pair of transport service access points;

— transfer of data.

Data Transfer Phase:

— sequencing;

— blocking;

— concatenation;

— segmenting;

— multiplexing or splitting;

— flow control;

— error detection;

— error recovery;

— expedited data transfer;

— transport service data unit delimiting;

— transport connection identification.

Release Phase:

— notification of reason for release;

— identification of transport connection release;

— transfer of data.

### Transport Layer Management

It is during the establishment phase that the transport layer establishes a transport connection between two session entities.

## 1.6   SESSION LAYER

When the session layer provides the transparent transfer of data units between entities it means that those session entities can behave as if they were physically co-located, although in reality they may be some considerable distance apart. It is as if they were communicating with each other face to face, totally unaware of the distance which separates them.The session layer adds the co-ordination of the dialogue (effectively the managing of the session itself) between the communicating presentation entities. It establishes a session connection when the presentation entities request one through a session services access point. This is no different from the technique employed within the other layers as far as service requests are concerned. There are two main services that the session layer must provide:

— establishment of the session connection;

— management of that connection.

The ISO reference model requires that the mapping of a session connection onto a transport connection should be one to one. This means that no multiplexing is allowed in the session layer. However, several session layers may use the same transport layer – but only sequentially (ie when one session is completed, another may begin using the same transport connection).

The complementary arrangement is also allowed: one session connection may use more than one transport connection. If a transport connection is broken because of problems with the network service, a new transport connection may be established without the session partners being aware of it. This means that the resynchronisation of the conversation between the session partners must be

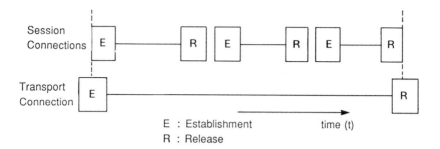

**Figure 1.10   Consecutive Session Connections**

handled entirely within the session layer itself. This can be illustrated more easily by referring to Figure 1.10 and 1.11. The interaction between the presentation entities is also the responsibility of the session layer, and certain rules must be agreed when a session connection is established so that each of the partners taking part in the session is aware of the rules and will abide by them. The reference model has defined three forms of interaction (following the lines of full duplex transmission, half duplex transmission and simplex transmission):

— two-way simultaneous (TWS), where both session partners can send and receive at the same time;

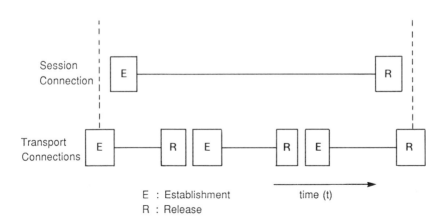

**Figure 1.11   Consecutive Transport Connections**

— two-way alternate (TWA), where session partners take turns, one
sending and one receiving;

— one-way, where only one presentation entity sends and the other
receives for the complete duration of the session connection.

The services provided by and the functions in the session layer can be
summarised as follows:

Services

— session connection establishment;

— session connection release;

— normal data exchange;

— quality of service;

— expedited data exchange:

  • two-way simultaneous,

  • two-way alternate,

  • one way;

— session connection synchronisation;

— exception reporting;

— additions in the reference model such as:

  • session service data unit sequencing numbering,

  • brackets,

  • stop,

  • go

  • security.

Functions

— mapping of session connection onto transport connection;

— session connection flow control;

— expedited data transfer;

— session connection recovery;

— session connection release;

— session layer management.

Once a communication session has been established the next step in the chain is to ensure that the data is presented in a meaningful way. It is nearly always possible to get people to talk to each other, but the art lies in getting them to understand each other. An analogy can be drawn with an engineering problem that needs to be solved through the participation of an English engineer who speaks only English and a Japanese engineer who speaks only Japanese. A session between the two engineers could easily be set up by using the telephone. However, the solution of the engineering problem, which was the reason for setting up the session, is unlikely to progress any further: neither party will understand the data being presented to him. Clearly the information needs to be presented in a meaningful way.

## 1.7 THE PRESENTATION LAYER

It is this layer which provides the solution, by giving services to the application layer related to the presentation of information in a form that is meaningful to the application entities. The reference model defines three syntactic versions of the data which is transferred between the application entities. These syntactic versions are:

— the syntax used by the originator;

— the syntax used by the receiver;

— the syntax used in the transfer process.

During the establishment of a presentation connection the entities must select and agree to the mapping between these syntaxes. If we take our previous problems with the English and Japanese engineers who speak only their own languages, the syntaxes at the originating and the receiving ends are English and Japanese respectively. Clearly a transfer syntax is required. In this case the transfer sytax can be any language, providing there is a capability to translate into English and into Japanese. The translator takes the part of the presentation entities on both sides (English and Japanese). Thus the services provided by the presentation layer relate to :

— the formatting of data (eg output data for a certain type of device);

— the transformation of data (ie the conversion of code/character sets by the presentation entities for the application entities);

— the selection of the transfer syntax to be used, negotiated when the presentation connection is established and possibly renegotiated during the existence of the connection.

A summary of the services provided by the functions of the presentation layer can be given as follows:

services

— data transformation;

— data formatting;

— syntax selection;

— presentation connections.

Functions

— general types:

  • session establishment request,

  • presentation image negotiation and renegotiation,

  • data transformation and formatting,

  • session termination request;

— addressing and multiplexing;

— presentation layer management.

The final layer in the ISO model which we will consider is the top layer – the application layer.

## 1.8   THE APPLICATION LAYER

The first thing to note about the application layer is that the application programs themselves do not reside in this layer, so its name is a little confusing. The purpose of the application layer is to provide services to the application programs (eg payroll programs, order processing software, etc). As the highest layer in the ISO reference model, the application layer provides a means for application processors to access the OSI environment.

Application processors exchange information by means of application entities, application protocols and presentation services. Figure 1.12 shows a schematic of the make-up of the application layer which comprises user

CASE  : Common Application Service Elements
SASE  : Specific Application Service Elements
        (may just be application service elements in the future)
FTAM  : File Transfer, Access and Management
JTM   : Job Transfer and Manipulation
VT    : Vertual Terminal

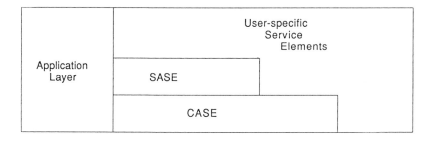

**Figure 1.12   Application Layer**

elements, common application service elements (CASE) and specific application service elements (SASE). Under the heading of specific application
service elements come file transfer, access and management (FTAM), job
transfer and manipulation (JTM) and virtual terminal (VT) facilities. Application services differ from services provided by other layers: they are not
provided to an upper layer or associated with a service access point. Services
may include the following, though some of the listed services are provided by
OSI management.

Services

— the identification of communications partners, for example by:

• address,

• generic description,

• definite description;

— determination of the availability of the intended communications
  partners;

— establishment of the authority to communicate;

— agreement on privacy;

— authentication of the intended communications partners;

— determination of cost allocation;

— determination of the provision of resources;

— determination of the quality of service, for example:

  • response time,

  • error rate,

  • cost (with respect to cost allocation);

— synchronisation of co-operating applications;

— selection of initiation and release procedures (including the ongoing dialogue);

— agreement on responsibility for error recovery;

— agreement on procedures for control of data integrity;

— identification of the constraints on character sets and data structure (data syntax).

**Functions**

The application layer contains all the functions involved in communication between open systems which are not already performed by the lower layers. This may seem to be a 'catch all' situation, but these functions do involve those performed by programs as well as those performed by human beings, and include systems management and applications management functions.

**1.9   MANAGEMENT**

Network management is critical within any system. When the system uses international standards with the potential for multi-vendor interworking, the subject becomes even more important. Unfortunately the network management work within ISO may not be completed for another five years.

The requirement for network management has been raised in the previous sections of this chapter on a layer-by-layer basis. This is not sufficient, as the layers must be able to provide information to a management utility. Figure 1.13 shows the relationship of the network management functions to the layers of the ISO model. A prerequisite of any open system will be that the layer interfaces are defined in such a way as to allow third party network management of the overall system.

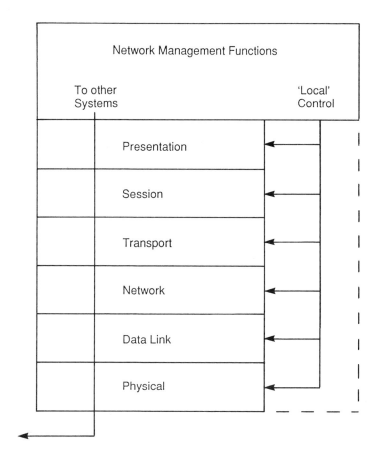

**Figure 1.13    Network Management Functions**

In addition, the network management functions must be able to interact not only with their own 'local' system but also with other 'remote' systems in order to provide a universal network management utility. Part of the local management requirement will usually reside within its own 'domain'.

Another crucial area of OSI is security. Suffice it to say that this subject is not suitably mature within the ISO to become a full international standard at the present time.

# 2 MAP Architecture

## 2.1 INTRODUCTION

Chapter 1 described the OSI seven-layer model and its layered structure. This chapter looks at the applications of that model in the industrial communications sector. The whole of the network architecture including the logical and physical qualities is based on the OSI seven-layer model. In this model each layer provides services for the layer above as described previously. There are two types of information which are transferred between the layers when these services are provided, these are control and data. The control information provides the basis for the layer services which are required in actually processing the message. This then allows the data to be transferred transparently between the layers with the exception of the presentation layer whose task is to reformat. Every layer adds on more protocol control information as it percolates down through the seven layers which will then be interpreted by the corresponding layer in the receiving node. Figure 2.1 shows the effect of this adding of information to the message as it progresses down from layer seven through to layer one. This process is reversed in the receiving node and the information which was previously added to the message is now stripped off as the message makes its way up from layer one through to layer seven.

## 2.2 THE ARCHITECTURE

It is a standard prerequisite of the MAP network that the actual physical cable must be accessible from every location in the plant. It follows that serviceability is a major factor when installing the cable and some areas which may well have needed to be serviced by the cable may be constrained by the type of cable used (for example, minimum bending radius).

It is impossible to foresee in the future every single situation where a MAP network may be required within a single plant. With this in mind, the whole of

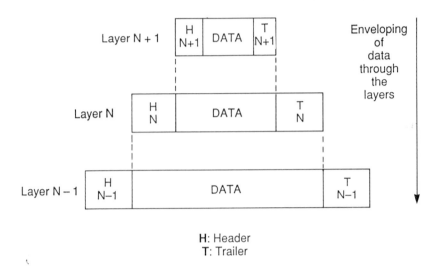

H: Header
T: Trailer

**Figure 2.1    Header and Trailer Information**

the network architecture may be implemented as a set of interconnected sub-networks which will also serve to keep the overall architecture within design and performance criteria. Geographic and organisational limitations may also require the creation of separately managed and maintained network segments. Figure 2.2 illustrates the type of overall network architecture which a MAP network may be required to fit into. This illustrates the need to interwork between different data systems and even to take account of the evolution of voice systems within the corporate infrastructure. Bridges or routers can connect two or more sub-networks, however, messages moving between two logically different sub-networks must be routed through router nodes based on network layer addressing. Network segments connected by MAP bridges can be considered as one single logical network.It is inevitable within the plant that non-MAP networks will have already evolved. These can be linked to the MAP sub-networks using gateways to access them which have a knowledge of both MAP and the non-MAP protocol.

The MAP network architecture therefore can be thought of as being made up of a number of functional building blocks which can be assembled to achieve the required results. These functional building blocks comprise:

— backbone architecture (MAP 'end' systems);

— cell architecture;

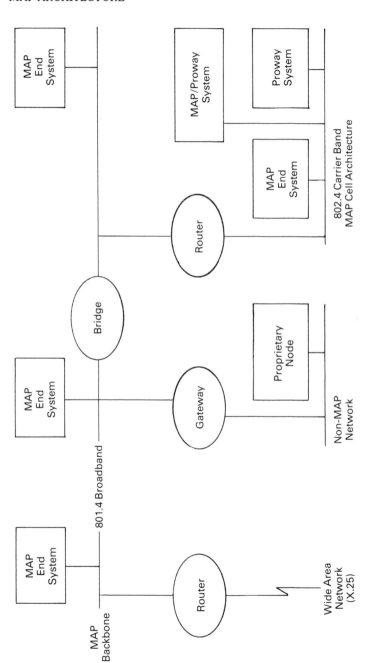

**Figure 2.2   Overall Network Architecture**

— MAP router;

— MAP bridge;

— MAP gateway;

— Mini-MAP system;

— MAP/EPA system.

The MAP backbone architecture is the simplest implementation of a MAP network. It involves a MAP backbone with cables running through each of the connected devices. It is typically suited to plants having requirements which are distributed over a large geographic area – the single backbone cable removing the requirement for multiple cables into connecting the devices. The MAP 'end' systems connected to the backbone architecture are nodes containing the full seven-layer implementation of the MAP architecture.

Equipment or machines performing discrete functions in the manufacturing process may be arranged into cells. Typically 95% of the information which is required to perform the discrete process within the cell will never need to leave the cell itself. The only information is likely to be command or response information to and from the cell and the shopfloor supervisory computer (for example, to download part programs and upload status information). The cell can be connected to the MAP backbone by means of a bridge, router or gateway. It will allow communications between the devices within the cell and any designated device elsewhere on the MAP network.

Routers connect two or more distinct networks at a common point and implement layers 1, 2 and 3 of the MAP architecture, as shown in Figure 2.3. They are not transparent and must be addressed to be used; however, they do have greater management facilities than bridges. A single common network address is applied to the router for all of the attached networks which may well operate independently of each other. Typically, routers are used to connect MAP networks to wide area networks, private branch exchanges and in all situations where the segmentation of link level frames is required.

The MAP bridge is used to connect two similar segments and hence extend the network beyond the original specification. Unlike the router the bridge is a transparent device and includes store and forward facilities. It operates at the data link level (layer 2) and is an ideal solution for connecting two segments similar in logical link control but differing in the physical layer, although the medium access control sub-layer must be the same in each node. The architecture of the bridge is illustrated in Figure 2.4. It is important to note that networks

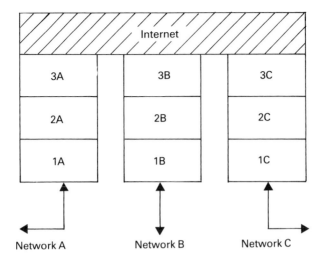

**Figure 2.3    Router Architecture**

built up from interlinked segments have a number of advantages which include:

— the segmentation can overcome limitations on the network distance and its capacity;

— faults can be restricted to individual segments;

— intelligent bridges (contrary to the description in its name) can act as isolators within a network. This can give a level of security and isolation.

A MAP gateway is used between MAP devices or segments and non-OSI or proprietary subnetworks. Its function allows communication between the two networks. The gateway utilises all seven layers of the OSI model as shown in Figure 2.5. Because the two networks which the gate interconnects are appreciably different, it must be able to:

— store and forward messages;

— provide flow control;

— provide a virtual circuit interface;

— support network management for the various subnetworks;

— performs protocol translation.

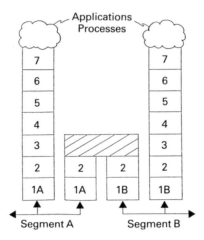

**Figure 2.4   Bridge Architecture**

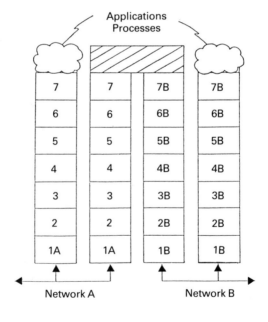

**Figure 2.5   Gateway Architecture**

The gateway is a non-transparent device and is connected at the application layer of the model. Gateways are not standard devices given the differences between various systems. This means that the gateway will have a different network address on each of the attached sub-networks.

The seven layers of the full MAP architecture are reduced to three layers in the mini-MAP system – layers 1, 2 and 7. A node which is based on this architecture, known as enhanced performance architecture, is a mini-MAP node. The architecture of such a node is shown in Figure 2.6. The objective of bypassing layers 3 to 6 means that faster message response times can be achieved. However, the application layer has to interface directly with the data link layer. The consequence of this is two-fold; first of all, mini-MAP nodes are not OSI compatible as they do not implement the full seven-layer architecture; and secondly, because the node bypasses four layers, it is starved of the services which these layers actually provide. Care needs to be taken when deciding on utilising mini-MAP nodes in that if you decide at the end of the day you need more functionality or services and try to implement them in layer 7 or above, so you are re-inventing the omitted layers. The use of mini-MAP must be carefully thought through.

MAP/EPA is a combination of MAP and EPA in a dual stack architecture.

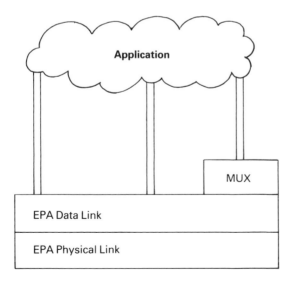

**Figure 2.6    Mini-MAP Node**

MAP/EPA is OSI compatible and a MAP/EPA node is a MAP device. Figure 2.7 illustrates this type of node and shows that on one side it implements the full seven layer MAP architecture while on the other it offers an open interface to layer 2. The MAP/EPA node can talk horizontally to other EPA nodes on the EPA side and to four seven layer nodes on the MAP side.

MAP, MAP/EPA and mini-MAP nodes must all use IEEE 802.4 services at the lower layers, allowing a bridge to be effectively used within MAP networks. Other aspects to the MAP architecture relate to broadband and carrier band.

A broadband cable which operates at 10Mbps can be connected to a carrier band cable operating at 5Mbps. The rotation time of the token itself of each interconnected segment is only increased by the addition of one extra node – the bridge. Different broadband channels can be connected together using a bridge. The design of the network, which would include taking account of performance

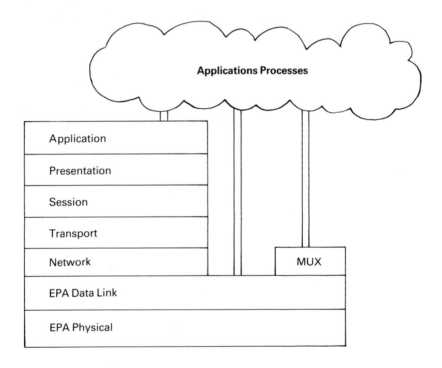

**Figure 2.7   MAP/EPA Architecture**

requirements, may involve separating one heavily loaded network into several smaller networks using interconnected bridges. Just as two broadband channels can be linked together, so can two carrier band segments.

The physical layout of networks which contain bridges are subject to restrictions:

— bridges must not form logical loops in networks even if physical loops are established;

— where bridges are connected in parallel, only one bridge would be allowed to relay messages to any one node at any one time.

The branching tree algorithm may be used to ensure these situations do not arise. Broadcast messages transmitted should be subject to the bridge restricting the flood of the message to all interconnecting segments save for the segment on which the message arrived. The bridge may do selective transmission of multicast addresses by utilising suitable parameters in a specific implementation and in addition may be programmed to ignore traffic bound for specific individual or multicast addresses. The bridge will not segment frames nor will it affect the frame size. There may be value added functions which a bridge could perform over and above those required by MAP which will provide useful user-aids which will assist in the operation of the network. Bridges may interconnect several segments. The interconnection of several segments may correspond to carrying several carrier band segments over a single broadband segment. In addition it may hold some of the network management functions. The non-MAP bridge is one of the connecting devices which do not have a MAP layer defined by IEEE 802.4. If the MAP layers are different it is recommended that a router is used.

The multi-vendor gateway is designed to provide protocol conversion between vendor specific protocols and the MAP network. Its objectives are as follows:

— it must provide a means of passing data between programmable devices and MAP nodes. This recognises the fact that programmable devices are almost certainly already installed on existing vendor specific networks;

— it must translate between the manufacturing message service (MMS) protocol and the vendor specific message formats;

— it must be bi-directional and be able to establish connections with other MAP nodes based on programmable device initiated messages;

— programmable devices which cannot initiate transmissions are assumed to be serviced by the host computer in its normal polling operation;

— it must be able to determine complete MAP addresses comprising physical, link, network, transport, session and the recipient's name of associated application processors in other MAP nodes with which the gateway is capable of establishing associations;

— it must service multiple, interleaved requests and responses for each application association;

— its application program must be capable of supporting multiple connections; the programmable device associated with each connection having been determined at the time the connection is made;

— it must accept as a minimum MMS conformance class 0 requests and execute them using whatever device specific operations are required, in turn generating MMS conformance class 0 responses.

The message flow from the MAP node to the programmable device takes the following steps:

1 The request is formulated into the manufacturing message service protocol in the MAP node.

2 The message is transferred to the lower levels of the MAP protocol stack.

3 The gateway receives the message via its MAP interface.

4 The presentation layer delivers the message to the gateway application program.

5 The gateway uses the information in the incoming MMS message to execute one or more vendor specific requests to the programmable device specified in the application association.

6 The gateway collects responses, if applicable, from the addressed programmable device and formulates a manufacturing message service response if required. It is this response which is then transferred to the requesting MAP application.

This chapter thus gives an overview of the components which are made up in the MAP architecture. It has been recognised that very few organisations have the benefits of implementing MAP in a 'greenfield' site, and account has been taken of connecting up to vendor specific architectures. After looking at the MAP specification in the next chapter (Chapter 3), the theme of MAP interworking with vendor specific implementations will continue through Chapter 4 and into Chapter 5. It cannot be emphasised too much that MAP must fit in with any organisation's plans for Computer Integrated Manufacturing. MAP should only be viewed as a means to an end and not taken purely as an elegant technical exercise. If the latter view is taken the overall business requirements will finish up very cloudy indeed. Chapter 3 discusses some of the main points brought out in the MAP specification.

# 3 MAP Specification

## 3.1 INTRODUCTION

Chapter 1 briefly explained the ISO OSI 7-layer reference model while Chapter 2 introduced the MAP architecture. This chapter describes the MAP specification, drawing comparisons, where appropriate, between the different versions of the MAP specification.

## 3.2 THE PHYSICAL LAYER

In the present version of the MAP specification, there are two physical layer options available for MAP compatible nodes:

—   802.4 broadband 10Mbps;

—   802.4 carrier band 5Mbps.

(Because of pressure from Europe it is inevitable that 802.3 will also be included.)

General Motors specified broadband in the earliest MAP draft (1.0) while the carrier band specification was introduced for draft version 2.2. In choosing broadband at the physical layer, General Motors were greatly influenced by the extent to which broadband was already used within their plants. In the future, two additional options are being developed:

—   802.4 on optical fibre using passive stars, 10Mbps and up to 32 ports;

—   802.5 on optical fibre with a reconfiguring dual ring configuration at 16Mbps and up to 100 stations.

The details of the fibre optic alternatives will not be considered in this chapter. However, the reader is directed towards the MAP specification for further details. In fact, the present book should be read in conjunction with the MAP specification. The design of a broadband network is not for do-it-yourself enthusiasts. To qualify this point, some of the key aspects of broadband will now be highlighted.

### 3.2.1  Broadband

Broadband is used to describe a coaxial cable system capable of carrying a wide bandwidth of radio frequencies. The coaxial cable may be dual or single. In this section we will consider the single option only. The bandwidth of the broadband cable is split into six MHz channels; each channel is separated from its neighbour by a distinct frequency, or they may coexist on a single coaxial cable simultaneously.

The channels themselves may support data signals, video or audio signals or a number of each, such that the total bandwidth of the network has been utilised. The broadband technology is part of the IEEE 802.4 (token passing bus) communication standard. It is recommended that the broadband technology is used for backbone networks and other multi-channel applications since, in effect, it allows multiple networks to coexist on the same media. In doing so, it minimises wiring modifications, an important aspect in any environment especially in the shopfloor environment, while effecting a smooth and orderly transition to MAP. Broadband networks can potentially carry a great many different services (see Figure 3.1). In order to take full effect of the cable bandwidth, channels must be assigned. Figure 3.3 shows the frequency allocation including those of MAP, while Figure 3.2 shows the channel assignments.

The basic communication medium of the broadband local area network is the coaxial cable, the technology of which is based on CATV (community antennae television) a well tried and tested technology and common in the USA. The cable uses a mid-split transmission technique; 40 channels of 6 megahertz outbound and 18 channels of 6 megahertz inbound. The system uses a forward frequency allocation of 174 to 300 megahertz and a reverse frequency allocation of 5 to 108 megahertz. It is possible to use multiple adjacent channels in order to carry wideband or high data rate services which require more than the normal channel bandwidth of 6 megahertz.

In the future, and as additional LAN devices are required on a system, it is expected that IEEE compatible equipment will become available in additional channels. By analysing the available spectrum it is clear that the inbound channels of both the FM bands will be the channels of choice for new

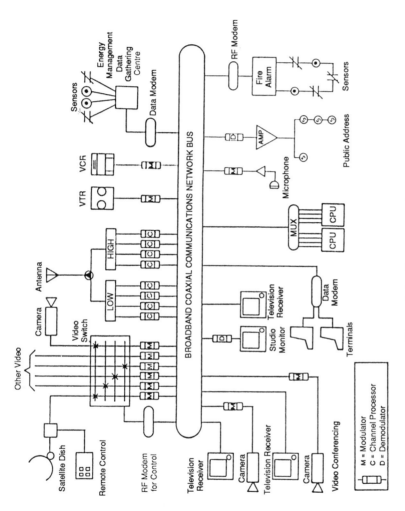

**Figure 3.1    Broadband Services**

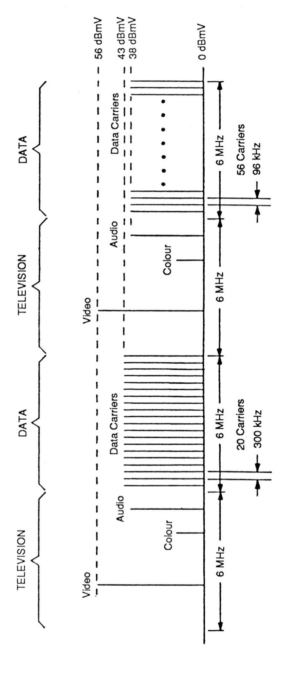

**Figure 3.2   Broadband Channel Assignments**

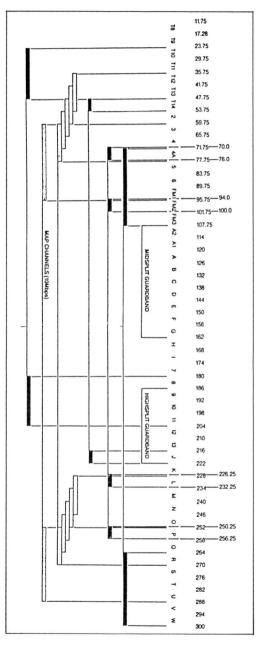

**Figure 3.3   Frequency Allocation**

frequencies. The channels are not available in mid-split systems so high-split systems will be required in order to take advantage of these expected devices. These high-split systems expand the availability of the two-way channels from 17 channels to a total of 22 or 24 and use a forward frequency allocation of 234 to 400+ megahertz and a reverse frequency allocation of 5 to 174 megahertz. Figure 3.4 shows the frequency allocation in relation to the broadband channels for the sub-split/mid-split format.

An important aspect of broadband is the cable layout. This is essentially a tree configuration. However, the tree can be designed in various ways in order to achieve specific design requirements, such as network partitioning or redundancy. A comparison of the configurations possible are:

— straight routeing of the cable covering the required geographical area for tap coverage, inserting amplifiers as and when necessary;

— the star configuration, locating all of the amplifiers within a single site and having cables running out to the attached devices in order to protect

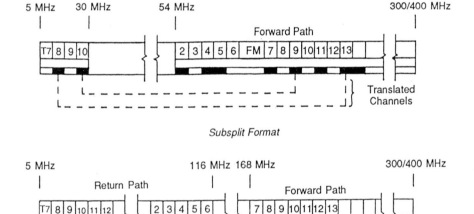

**Figure 3.4   Subsplit/Midsplit Formats**

all of the amplifiers on one site and ease the maintenance problem. Since they are in a more controlled environment there is the potential for higher reliability also. The disadvantage of this topology is that the network will require more cable and amplifiers than a similar network using a non-star configuration. An example of this configuration is shown in Figure 3.5;

— for large sites a distributed star may be used. It is basically the same as the topology described above, but is repeated with clusters of amplifiers placed around the plant, each being connected to the head-end via a trunk cable. Figure 3.6 shows this distributed star network topology;

— for multiple plant networks, or even very large sites, a combination of trunk cables and distributed stars can be used.

When designing any cable system the objective is to choose components, optimise performance within the specified range of design parameters and stay within the system cost. The basic coaxial cable system is shown in Figure 3.7. Specialist cable suppliers and installers will provide the system network design in order to optimise these parameters. This will include positioning the head-end to allow for the size of the network and location of existing equipment. In large networks the head-end may be placed in a central location in order to

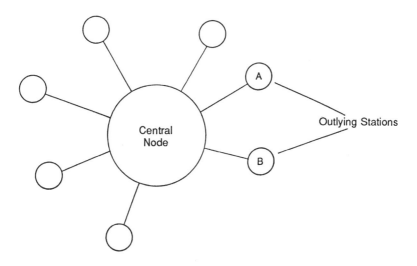

**Figure 3.5   Star Configuration**

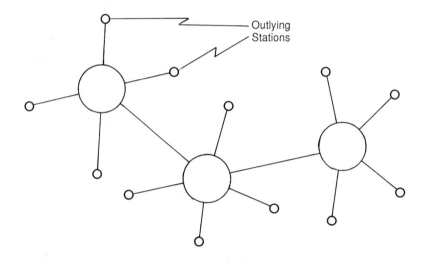

**Figure 3.6    Distributed Star**

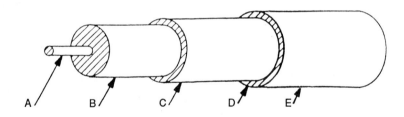

A    CENTRE CONDUCTOR: Centremost feature of coaxial cable, it consists of solid copper or copper clad aluminium wire.

B    DIELECTRIC: Electrical insulation utilised to maintain position of the centre conductor. It is composed of foamed polyethlene. This insulator/positioner may also be evenly spaced polyethylene discs.

C    OUTER CONDUCTOR: Is constructed of an aluminium tube. The cable size (412, 500, 750 & 1000) is derived from its outside diameter.

D    FLOODING COMPOUND: (OPTIONAL) A viscous substance placed between the outer conductor C and the jacket E to maintain a protective seal should the jacket E contain or develop any cuts or openings.

E    JACKET: (OPTIONAL) A black polyethylene coating over the aluminium outer conductor to provide a weather-tight seal.

**Figure 3.7    Coaxial Trunk Cable**

minimise the number of amplifiers required. However, in general the head-end would be placed in or near the primary computer centre.

Each head-end can have multiple ports which are translated (permitting connection of communication devices which transmit on to the cable system through a retransmission device at the head-end) or untranslated (permitting the connection of devices which transmit directly out on to the cable network from the head-end to similar devices connected to taps elsewhere in the network in a point-to-point fashion). The components of a simple complete head-end are shown in Figure 3.8 as an example. Head-end ports will be divided into identifiable input and output ports as some interface units or devices require separate input and output ports with adequate isolation between them.

Multiple head-ends may be provided on some networks allowing each head-end to communicate with any device on the network, with the exception of the network ports on the other head-ends. This type of configuration may be used where computer, control or monitoring centres for the various services are geographically spread. As stated previously, broadband design is a specialised area. Some of the aspects of broadband design which will be taken into consideration are:

— **Serviceability:** to allow for the physical considerations including positioning of the network equipment (amplifier location for the ease of servicing) and equipment test points;

— **Path loss:** as any electromagnetic signal is subject to attenuation, the

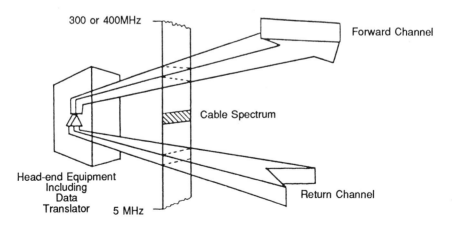

**Figure 3.8    Head-End**

considerations for a balanced network design need to be taken care of. this must be allowed for over the total operational frequency range;

— **Frequency response:** allowing for the gain response of the channel over the usable frequency spectrum, separately measured for both the inbound and outbound paths;

— **Transmit signal level:** critical if a balanced network is to be obtained is the signal level at the input of the network as all other gains or losses on the network are relative to this;

— **Carrier to noise ratio:** measured at any head-end port (the inbound carrier to noise ratio) relative to the carrier signal input to any remote distribution user port measured in a specific bandwidth. A similar measurement must apply to the outbound carrier to noise ratio;

— **Distortion:** always present and requiring addressing when any non-linear components are used in any design;

— **Home modulation:** can be the product of imperfect amplifier power supply filtering and any component non-linearity;

— **Return loss:** broadband cable systems are impedance matched systems, meaning that if the characteristic impedance of the components in the system do not match the impedance of the system, part of the signal power will be reflected back to the source;

— **Outlet-to-outlet isolation:** design parameters must specify the isolation between any two user ports at all of the frequencies in the inbound and outbound paths.

Listing these aspects in broadband design is not meant to frighten the reader, merely to point out that the correct design of a broadband network is a specialist activity. The activity should be carried out by qualified personnel and any perceived expansion to the network allowed for from day one when possible.

Another important aspect of implementing a broadband network lies in the support of that network. It should not be overlooked that a broadband network would require specially trained staff or maintenance contracts so as to carry out periodic network testing, eg frequency sweeps and preventative maintenance. Given that the broadband network may be viewed as a utility within the plant in much the same way as gas, electricity or water, the interface to the other plant services (for example, slow scan TV, time recording, security) should not be overlooked.

## 3.2.2 Carrier Band

This technology on coaxial cable is recommended for single channel networks and subnetworks. It uses less expensive and less complex hardware from multivendor installations and can be used in situations where the full bandwidth of broadband is not required, for example in cells. Broadband technology uses two different frequencies, one to transmit and the second to receive. In order to achieve this, a frequency translator is needed in addition to tightly tuned high frequency filters, radio frequency modulators and radio frequency mixers making broadband not cost effective where only a single channel is required. The carrier band modulation scheme, on the other hand, is a single channel system with the entire bandwidth reserved for the one network. It does not need to be tuned at each individual station and so is easier to install, making it more robust in the harsh environment of shopfloor cells. There is no requirement for a head-end on the network since data is transmitted and received on the same channel – the head-end previously doing the frequency translation. The physical characteristics of carrier band are cheaper because it can be designed and implemented with normal digital logic and a small amount of the complex radio frequency analogue circuitry.

Carrier band technology is part of the IEEE 802.4 communication standard. The modulation technique is phase coherent as specified by IEEE 802.4 and the data rate for carrier band is 5Mbps. Carrier band supports bi-directional transmission and the delay between transmission from a node and reception by another node is limited to the propagation delays induced by the medium itself. A single carrier band segment does have physical limitations due to the attenuation induced by the cables and taps, however, with regenerative repeating there is no limit to the size or number of stations on a carrier band network. For carrier band the following guidelines have been given for implementation purposes:

— a maximum of 32 stations connected to one cable segment;

— the maximum distance between the most remote stations in the logical ring should not exceed 700 metres on RG-11 cable;

— the cables are those commonly used within the CATV industry which utilise the single channel phase coherent frequency shift keying;

— the drop cables should be flexible RG-11, RG-6 or RG-59 and should not exceed 50 metres in length.

The MAP/TOP media committee is investigating carrier band and the reader is directed to the findings of this committee regarding installation and media selection guidelines.

## 3.3 THE DATA LINK LAYER

This layer is divided into two sub-layers:

— the media access control sub-layer (MAC);

— the logical link control sub-layer (LLC).

The chosen media access control method for the MAP specification is IEEE 802.4 (token passing bus). Although this is physically a token passing bus it can be logically thought of as a ring for the purpose of passing the token. The principle of the logical ring on a physical bus is shown in Figure 3.9. The token passing bus method is deterministic, meaning that the time it takes a message to get from one node to another can be exactly determined. The MAC sub-layer is responsible for the handling of the token and sharing the bus with other stations. In addition to this it receives data from the layers directly above and below the data link layer for transmission either across the network or to the user.

The preferred standard in the MAP specification for the logical link control (LLC) sub-layer is the IEEE 802.4 specification. This defines the multipoint peer-to-peer protocol. In MAP version 2.1 two types of service are specified within this sub-layer. However, in MAP version 3.0 three types of service are

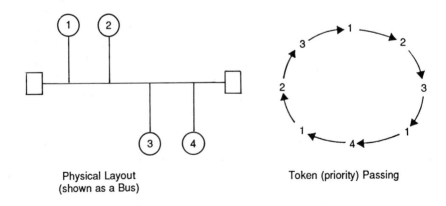

Physical Layout
(shown as a Bus)

Token (priority) Passing

**Figure 3.9  Logical Ring on a Physical Bus**

available. The two types of service specified in both the earlier version of MAP and version 3.0 are:

— Connectionless oriented (type 1);

— Connection oriented (type 2).

The additional third type specified in version 3.0 of the MAP specification is:

— Acknowledged connectionless oriented (type 3).

The connectionless oriented service allows for data exchange between two LLC entities without establishing the data link connection. However, the service does not provide for message sequencing, acknowledgement, flow control or error recovery. The connection oriented service, on the other hand, does establish a data link connection and provides message sequencing acknowledgement, flow control and error recovery. The third type acknowledged connectionless oriented service allows for limited frame acknowledgement, limited flow control and retransmission on a single frame basis. In addition to the three types there are also three classes of service specified:

— that which supports type 1 operation only (class 1);

— that which supports operation types 1 and 2 (class 2);

— that which supports operations 1 and 3 (class 3).

MAP specifies connectionless oriented class 1 service or if the acknowledgements are required, class 3 service. If EPA is used for a faster network response there may be a need to use class 3. When no higher layers exist, the LLC sublayer needs to assume the responsibility of error handling which, in the presence of higher layers, would be accepted by those layers. As described above, class 3 supports both type 1 and type 3 systems, providing the necessary error handling in mini-MAP and MAP/EPA nodes. In the process control environment the use of time-critical applications gives rise to a need for the message to be acknowledged so the plant and the process can be properly controlled. The data link layer, as described in MAP version 3.0 will support immediate acknowledgement options as well as a message priority scheme. Clearly, this is advisable for use in time critical applications and illustrates the influence of the process control industry on the evolution of the MAP specification.

## 3.4   THE NETWORK LAYER

The OSI network service is provided at the boundary between the network layer and the transport layer. This service provides for the transparent transfer of data between network service users. There are two types of OSI network service:

— Connectionless oriented network service (CLNS);

— Connection oriented network service (CONS).

MAP networks support only the connectionless mode network service. In accordance with the internal organisation of the network layer it is divided into three roles. These are:

— sub-network access protocol (SNACP);

— sub-network dependent convergence protocol (SNDCP);

— sub-network independent convergence protocol (SNICP).

The SNACP provides the necessary interface to the data link layer. In the case of MAP end systems a discrete SNACP is not required. The SNDCP adjusts upward or downward the services provided by the SNACP. In doing this, it is used to provide the services assumed by the SNICP or to provide the network service directly. A protocol for filling the SNICP role operates to construct the OSI network service over a well-defined set of underlying capabilities. For providing the connectionless mode network protocol (SLNP) the ISO 8473 protocol will be used. This provides the services of the internet sub-layer in MAP version 2.1. In MAP version 3.0 ISO 8473 P-CLNS is now an international standard. The full ISO 8473 conformance protocol will be used with the following exceptions:

— the inactive subset for intra sub-network communication will not be supported. Protocol data units (PDU) which have been encoded using the inactive subset in implementations will not be transmitted. Received PDUs encoded using the inactive subset will be discarded;

— the non-segmenting subset will not be used. Implementations will not generate PDUs without a segmentation path. However, they will receive and correctly process PDUs which do contain the segmentation path.

In MAP version 2.1, the inclusion of these subsets allowed systems on the same local area network to communicate without segmentation of data units at the network layer. This is not available in MAP version 3.0. The European MAP Users Group (EMUG) suggests that the inactive network protocol should be left in the MAP specification since its omission will reduce performance when a complete utilisation of the network layer is not taken up.

In MAP version 3.0, the type 2 functions of security, complete source routeing and complete route record are not supported as is the case with MAP version 2.1. The PDU containing such a parameter is discarded and replaced with an error PDU. All of the type 3 functions are optional for end systems. For the intermediate systems, all type 3 functions are optional except partial route record which must be supported.

The routeing mechanism is the process of determining the sub-network point of attachment (SNPA) of the next hop which a data packet must take in order to get to the destination network service access point (NSAP). The routeing in MAP networks can be divided into three basic levels:

— the routeing between enterprises (an enterprise being effectively a factory or plant);

— the routeing between sub-networks within an enterprise;

— the routeing between end systems and intermediate systems within a sub-network.

This task is made easier by dividing the NSAP address into three logical sections:

— the enterprise ID to identify an enterprise;

— intermediate system to intermediate system in order to identify a sub-network;

— end system to intermediate system in order to identify an end system.

The ISO end system to intermediate system protocol is supported as a mandatory protocol in order to facilitate dynamic routeing. This facility was not supported in version 2.1 of the MAP specification. However, its presence in MAP version 3.0 allows end systems to obtain addresses of intermediate systems reachable in one hop. The facility also allows intermediate systems to obtain the addresses of all of the end systems on its sub-networks.

No suitable protocol is available for intermediate system to intermediate system routeing. This means that intermediate systems must keep static tables of other reachable intermediate systems. It is clear that a protocol is required and is now under examination to be included in MAP as the specification matures.

Over MAP local area networks the following agreements apply to the use of end systems to intermediate systems exchange protocols:

— the implementations involved must support any valid NSAP address format;

— the implementations must support configuration information and route re-direction information with no subsets permitted;

— local systems management must be capable of setting all time values;

— local system management must be capable of setting the use of checksums which under normal use will be disabled;

— the intermediate systems must transmit quality of service, security and priority fields in protocol data units if they are present in the data which generated the re-direction. However, the end systems must ignore them in a received protocol data unit;

— end systems and intermediate systems must support the use of optimisation for system initialisation.

It is also specified in MAP that all MAP systems must use binary syntax for the domain specific part. However, systems must accept both binary and decimal.

In order to achieve connection oriented to connectionless oriented sub-network connections a CLNP router will be used which will utilise an SNDCP. For future direction a three-layer intermediate system with an interworking function residing above layer 3 is currently being considered.

## 3.5    THE TRANSPORT LAYER

In MAP version 3.0 the transport layer is defined by class 4 of the ISO compatible subset of the National Bureau of Standards, class 4 transport protocol specifications (ISO 8073), and the transport service definition (ISO 8072). In order to provide some compensation for the functions lost by using a connectionless service for the data link layer, the MAP specification defines the largest and richest class of transport, class 4. As well as connection, data transfer and disconnection, as provided by class 0, the simplest class of transport, class 4 also provides multiplexing of transport connections, flow control, checking for out of sequence data, an expedited data service, error detection and resynchronisation after errors. The four classes of transport protocol are shown in Figure 3.10. Although layer 4 of the MAP specification defines the OSI compatible subset there are fundamental differences between the ISO and NBS standards relating to:

Class 0 : Simple Class, no enhancement to the network service
Class 1 : Basic Error Recovery Class
Class 2 : Multiplexing Class
Class 3 : Error Recovery and Multiplexing Class
Class 4 : Error Detection and Recovery Class

**Figure 3.10    Classes of Transport Service**

— the NBS standards support the concept of datagrams allowing a transport user to transport data to a corresponding user without establishing a transport connection;

— a graceful close of a connection is provided by the NBS standard (although it is redundant with the session protocol) whereas the ISO standard does not support this;

— the status of the connections are not supported by the ISO standard.

Although the protocol in MAP version 3.0 is very similar to that in MAP version 2.1 a few extra amendments have been made. In addition, as a consequence of using a connection oriented network service (CONS) over X.25, consideration is being given to the inclusion of class 0 protocol.

## 3.6   THE SESSION LAYER

At the session layer MAP specifies the ISO session standard using full duplex communication. In pre-MAP version 3.0 a subset of the basic combined sub-set (BCS) was all that was required to support the higher layer services. With the scope of the applications increasing, additional layer functions are being introduced. The basic activity subset (BAS) provides all of the basic combined subset capabilities with the addition of exception reporting, some synchronisation and activity management. The MAP version 3.0 specification defines the session layer as comprising three stages:

— session connection establishment;

— data transfer;

— session connection release.

Session layer services which are made available to the presentation layer are defined in terms of functional units. These are logical groupings of related services and are negotiated by the peer session service users during the connection establishment phase. For MAP connectivity the minimum subset of the ISO session international standard is specified by the kernel functional unit and the duplex functional unit (the optional resynchronise functional unit is now available). A proposed addendum to the session international standard is the removal of length restriction on S_connect session protocol data unit (SPDU). The following rules must be adhered to in order for session layer implementations to be in conformance with the MAP specification:

— the required session of functional units must be included in all MAP systems and implemented in accordance with documented agreements;

— the documents listed in the specification shall be used as the supporting documents for implementing the MAP session layer protocol;

— as well as meeting all of the requirements of the specification a conforming implementation must conform to ISO as well.

In addition, MAP also mandates that the applicable rules of extensibility are followed. These rules are:

— unknown parameters in an otherwise known PDU should be ignored;

— if the length of a known parameter is longer than expected the additonal data should be ignored.

## 3.7 THE PRESENTATION LAYER

The objective of this layer is to carry out the negotiation of transfer syntaxes and to provide for the transformation to and from transfer syntaxes.

The most immediate major difference between MAP version 2.1 and MAP version 3.0 is the inclusion of the kernel presentation service into the specification, together with the use of abstract syntax notation 1 (ASN.1) encoding in certain application service and protocol standards. The abstract syntax notation 1 language is used to define the type and values of a data item and collection of data items without specifying the exact bit representation of the information. The presentation kernel services allow for the establishment of a connection which will use a selected encoding of a selected abstract syntax. The MAP version 3.0 specification is entirely devoted to the issues involved with the negotiation of transfer syntaxes and the responsibilities of the presentation protocol and as such covers the protocol agreements. The following functional unit is required for all systems:

— presentation kernel functional units support the basic presentation services required in order to establish a presentation connection, transfer normal data and then release the presentation connection. This is a non-negotiable functional unit.

For the implementation encompassing file transfer, access and management (FTAM) application service element (ASE) the following abstract syntaxes must be supported:

— ISO 8571-FTAM;

— ISO 8650-2-ACSE1;

— NBS-AS1.

In addition to these the following abstract syntaxes are also defined (however, these are optional within the agreements):

— NBS-AS2;

— NBS-AS3.

As far as manufacturing message service (EIA-511) ASE implementations are concerned, the following abstract syntaxes must be supported:

— MMS;

— ISO 8650-2-ACSE1.

For MAP network management ASE implementation the following abstract syntaxes must be supported:

— MAP/TOP-systems-management-protocol;

— ISO 8650-2-ACSE1.

For an ISO-CCITT directory service implementation the following abstract syntaxes must be supported:

— ISO-DP 9594-1986;

— ISO 8650-2-ACSE1.

The application programs which use the application context name PRIVATE shall use the following abstract syntax:

— PRIVATE.

The abstract syntaxes mentioned above are proposed names and must subsequently be assigned by the appropriate registration authority. All mandatory and optional abstract syntaxes must support the following transfer syntax:

— NBS/TS1.

Any other transfer syntax may also be implemented. In addition MAP also mandates that the applicable rules of extensibility are followed, which are:

— unknown parameters in an otherwise known PDU should be ignored;

— if the length of a known parameter is longer than expected the additional data should be ignored.

### 3.8    THE APPLICATION LAYER

Common application service elements (CASE) include a set of association control service elements (ACSE). The association control elements are included in MAP version 3.0 and provide for connection establishment and connection release to manage inter-application communication. ACSE is intended to provide a standard service for applications to communicate common parameters such as titles, addresses and application context during the request for an association. The reader is directed to the MAP specification for a list of the ACSE service primitives.

The MAP application context will only specify the rules governing the use of a single application service element (ASE) with ACSE on an application association.

The application context name PRIVATE is available for use as a default value. The MAP specification recognises the following application context:

— ISO FTAM;

— EIA 511 (manufacturing message service);

— MAP/TOP network management;

— ISO-CCITT directory services;

— PRIVATE.

It is also feasible that any other application context may be supported if the names are registered with the registration authority. Common application service elements provides common facilities required by specific application service elements (SASE) although FTAM, for example, did not use CASE-

ACSE until MAP version 3.0. The details of the rules governing the application entities (AE) are given in the MAP specification.

## 3.9   MAP DIRECTORY SERVICES

The Directory Service specification in MAP version 3.0 solves the directory needs of the single enterprise domain. It is a future work item to address the multiple enterprise domain problem.

A MAP network must have the capability of translating normal user initiated names to computer usable addresses. This table of names and addresses is the MAP directory database. The MAP Directory system allows user friendly references to network objects, giving a more stable network. Additions, deletions and changes in the physical location of network objects remain invisible to users who use directory services.

— The Directory system consists of the following elements:

— Directory Information Base (DIB);

— Directory Service Agent (DSA);

— Directory User Agent (DUA);

— User.

A user is able to update as well as question the Directory system in MAP version 3.0 (depending on security status), whereas it was only possible to read from the DIB in version 2.1. The Directory system is not meant to be a general purpose database. It is assumed there will be a higher frequency of queries than updates to the system. There is no need for instantaneous global updates; transient conditions where both old and new versions of the same information are available are quite acceptable.

A client issues an update or query to its DUA, which forwards the request to a DSA using the Directory Access Protocol (DAP). A collection of information is maintained by the Directory system in the DIB. In order to satisfy the requirements for the distribution and management of the DIB, and to ensure that objects can be unambiguously named and their entries found, a flat structure of entries is not possible. Therefore, a hierarchical structure is used, with the DIB being accessed through the DSA.

There are two kinds of entries, object entries and alias entries. For any particular object there is one object entry, this being the primary collection of information in the DIB about that object. In addition there may be zero or more alias entries for that object, the alias being used to provide alternative names for objects. An entry consists primarily of a set of attributes which are the individual items of information held in the entry, each describing a particular characteristic of an object. Each DUA logically serves a single user so that the Directory system may control access to directory information on the basis of DUA names.

MAP recognises three representations of the Directory system based on the number and functionality of DSAs. A 'centralised' implementation consists of a single DSA. Queries from all DUAs on the system are made to this DSA. A 'stand-alone' implementation is one wherein there may be more than one DSA, but the DSAs handle queries from DUAs only. They do not query or make reference to any other DSA on the system. A 'fully distributed' implementation is one wherein there can be several DSAs in the system, each capable of making queries to or handling queries from other DSAs, such as by hinting, chaining, multicasting, and decomposition.

*Hinting* is a process whereby the contacted DSA is unable to resolve the DUA request. The DSA replies by sending a hint consisting of an alternative DSA which may be able to resolve the DUA request. This technique puts the burden of the search on the DUA.

*Chaining* is a process whereby the DSA contacts another DSA who may be able to resolve the request. The contacted DSA may in turn contact another DSA. This technique puts the burden of the search on the DSAs.

*Multicasting* involves sending identical queries to more than one DSA, and is used when it is not known which DSA is most likely to have the answer.

*Query decomposition* involves splitting a query into a number of different queries, and sending them to the appropriate DSAs. It is used when the information required is distributed among several DSAs.

*Shadowing* involves maintaining copies of portions of the DIB by other DSAs separate from the DSA that maintains the master copy.

A DSA may enhance its ability to satisfy query operations locally, or to navigate operations more directly to other DSAs, as a result of holding information obtained from query operations to other DSAs. This is known as *caching*.

The directory must be able to determine if a user has the right to perform the specific request for service on the referenced information. The only externally visible behaviour is an error message if the access was denied. Access to a protected item is controlled in the following way:

— the type of the item governs what kinds of access are possible to the item, and therefore what access categories are defined;

— the owner or administrator of the item establishes and maintains an access control list for the item;

— when an accessor attempts to access the item, a check is made that, in the access control list for the item, there is at least one value which allows that particular accessor, identified by its distinguished name, to make that particular category of access.

Each service is provided by means of a sequence of conceptual interactions called service primitives. There are two types of service capabilities:

— some service capabilities are associated with several services and such a capability is represented in a service by a specific parameter;

— some service capabilities are associated with a specific service. Several capabilities may be associated with the same service.

The following is a summary of the service capabilities required as part of several services:

— name handling (verification);

— collection of objects handling;

— service and access control.

The following is a summary of the service capabilities related to a single service:

— read entry;

— check and/or alter membership;

— add or remove an object, its attributes and aliases.

Two peer protocols operate in the Directory system:

— Directory Access Protocol defines the exchange of requests and responses between a DUA and DSA;

— Directory System Protocol defines the exchange of requests and responses between two DSAs.

These are CCITT/ISO standards rather than special MAP designed protocols as used in version 2.1.

A MAP version 3.0 Directory implementation must conform to one of the three conformance classes. In general, conformance classes 0 and 1 specify single (stand-alone) DSA implementation with a centralised DIB. Conformance class 2 allows for multiple DSAs and distributed operations. Class 0 will typically meet the following Directory requirements:

a) MAP installations.

b) FTAM directory requirements.

The implementation must support the Directory access protocol. Unrestricted access by all users must be allowed hence the DS-Access-Control-Error is never generated. Conformance classes other than class 0 are not required for MAP installations.

A DSA implementation is required to recognise all service elements. Conformance to a class means the DSA processes only the service elements required for that class. In order for communication to be carried out between a DUA and a DSA or between two DSAs an association has to be established between the corresponding application entities. The association management services are concerned with establishing and terminating connections. The association management services are DS-BIND and DS-UNBIND. DS-BIND initialises a dialogue between the service user and the service provider. DS-UNBIND finalises a connection.

The Directory is completely located in the application layer of the 7 layer model. Most MAP implementations will map the remote service operations onto ACSE and presentation data transfer. A directory management domain is composed of at least one DSA with zero or more DUAs.

The Remote Operation Service (ROS) is provided by a sublayer which is in the application layer of the OSI model. A fundamental characteristic of the remote service operation is that it separates the OSI service from the application entity. Its functionality is to provide a mechanism by which a pair of Remote Operation Service users can establish a ROS association with each other and hence one ROS user can request operations from or perform operations for the other ROS user.

The basic ROS services support only class 1 and 2 operations. This means that only operations reporting result or error are supported in a synchronous or asynchronous mode of operation. In addition, the basic ROS services support only class 1 association. That means only the ROS user initiating a ROS association may invoke operations.

Only basic connection-oriented communications have been considered. This satisfies the current most urgent need. However, the use of other styles of communication to support remote operations is for further urgent study, and may include the following:

— asynchronous communication via store and forwarding messaging services;

— connection-oriented transaction processing;

— unit-operations;

— mapping onto connectionless mode communication services;

— multi-endpoint communication (multicast) of all of the above kinds;

— integration of CCR provisions (Commitment, Concurrency and Recovery) with use of remote operations in the varied styles above.

An application entity invokes operations provided by another entering into an exchange of Operation Protocol Data Units (OPDUs). The mapping onto CASE uses the basic kernel subset of CASE and the presentation kernel functional unit of the presentation service.

**CASE Association Establishment**

A ROS-entity attempts CASE association establishment in response to a bind request when no CASE association is available to be re-used. The A-ASSOCI-ATE response is used to establish an association between two ROS-entities. It is a confirmed service.

**Data Transfer Phase**

Each OPDU is conveyed using the Presentation P-DATA service. An OPDU is transferred as a single OPDU. If the receiving ROS-entity detects a problem during receipt of an OPDU, which cannot be resolved with the reject mechanism, it may issue an A_U_ABORT request. Aborting the CASE association is the most severe action.

**CASE Association Release**

The ROS-entity may issue an A_RELEASE request response to an UNBIND request. Upon receiving an A_RELEASE indication, the ROS-entity issues an UNBIND indication. Upon receiving the UNBIND response, the ROS-entity issues an A_RELEASE response. Upon receiving an A_RELEASE confirm, the ROS-entity issues an UNBIND confirm. The A_RELEASE service is a confirmed service. If the ROS-entity detects a serious problem, which cannot be resolved with the reject mechanism, it may issue an A_U_ABORT request. It is a local matter as to how the ROS-user is told that the ROS-association is lost. The A_U_ABORT service is an unconfirmed service.

The CASE-provider may abort an association for any of a variety of reasons (for example, transport connection failure or local or remote provider problem), indicated by a reason parameter. The ROS user is informed about this by the REJECT_P primitive. A common use of a directory is to supply the presentation address of an application entity. A query supplies an AE title and receive back a set of selectors and NSAP address.

Two directory services are required:

— the application title directory service that processes an AE title and gives the addressing information at the network service and the layers above required to access the AE;

— the network address directory service that processes a network-address and provides the information used below the network service boundary to access the NSAP.

The input to the application title directory service is an AE title. There are two components in the service:

— a name resolver which can resolve an AE title that is a descriptive name into the AE title that is a primitive name of the AE;

— a directory which returns the information associated with an AE title that is a primitive name.

The input to the network address directory service is a network-address which is a primitive name. Using the network address as input to the service results in the associated addressing information necessary at the network layer and the layers below.

## File Transfer Access and Management

The FTAM specification provides a set of services for conveniently transferring information between application processes and filestores. It guarantees the ability to:

— work with binary or text files;

— create files;

— delete files;

— transfer entire files;

— read file attributes;

— change file attributes;

— erase file contents;

— locate specific records;

— read and write records of a file.

In addition the following file types may be optionally supported:

— sequential files;

— random access files;

— single key indexed sequential files.

The FTAM standard defines a virtual filestore which is used for describing the service provided by the FTAM service element. The virtual filestore is used to map FTAM services onto the local filestore.

Initially, FTAM included only the kernel read and write functions, together with the limited file management and restrictions on file size and data formats. The MAP 3.0 FTAM will be provided as part of an application entity type which contains the FTAM service element and the ACSE service element. The addition of ACSE and, more importantly, the presentation layer will allow the manipulation of more file formats and some record-level access. Neither the FTAM standard nor NBSIR 86-3385 (based on ISO 8571 DIS) specify an interface to the FTAM services. The definition of an interface to the FTAM services is left to the implementor.

For an implementation of FTAM to be conformant to this specification it must be conformant to the documentation. In addition, general-purpose devices must have each of the following features:

— act as both initiator and responder;

— act as both sender and receiver;

— support the transfer, management, transfer and management and access service classes.

## Manufacturing Message Service

The Manufacturing Message Service (MMS) is a communications protocol standard for manufacturing applications. MMS resides in the application layer of the OSI seven-layer model.

Although MMS is applicable to a wide range of plant applications, the specification does not contain information on specific applications. Thus MMS is a horizontal standard, in that it specifies how messages are assembled and sent, but it does not contain application-specific information. The application-specific information necessary for interoperability of plant floor equipment is intended to be supplied by companion standards to MMS.

The control and monitoring of a manufacturing process is a distributed information processing task. In order to successfully carry out this task, inter-operation of a number of open systems is required (an open system is defined as a set of computers and associated software, including peripherals, terminals, human operators, physical processes, etc that complies with the requirements of OSI standards in its communications with other systems).

In Open Systems Interconnection, the interoperation of open systems is modelled in terms of the interactions between application processes in these systems. The distributed task of control and monitoring of a manufacturing process requires the cooperation of two or more application processes.

Several requirements must be met to allow the cooperative operation of application processes. First, they must share sufficient information to enable them to interact and carry out processing functions in a compatible and cooperative manner. In order to allow successful interworking between application processes, they must share a common understanding of their manufacturing environment. It is convenient to describe the model of the manufacturing environment in terms of a set of abstract 'objects'. Examples of objects in the manufacturing environment include variables, programs and semaphores.

As an Application Service Element (ASE), MMS makes use of and maps onto the services and service primitives of Association Control Service Elements (ACSE) and the Presentation Layer. All MMS Protocol Data Units (PDUs) shall be carried as user data on an ACSE or presentation service primitive.

## Context Management

The context management service contains the initiate, conclude, abort, cancel and reject services. These services allow the Manufacturing Message Standard (MMS) user:

1 To initiate communication with another MMS user in the MMS context, and to establish the requirements and capabilities that support that communication;

2 To conclude communication with another MMS user in the MMS context in a graceful manner;

3 To abort communications with another MMS user in the MMS context in an abrupt manner;

4 To cancel pending service requests; and

5 To receive notification of protocol errors that occur.

The context management handles the management of all MMS connection services.

## File Management

The MMS file management services provide necessary functionality for reading files containing control programs and data from filestores in control devices and file servers, and for managing filestores by enumerating the names and attributes of files, renaming, and deleting files.

MMS file services define the necessary functionality for reading and managing files. This functionality is modelled in relation to the MMS virtual filestore. The MMS virtual filestore is a container for a collection of files and a specification of the attributes and properties of those files.

When more extensive file services are required, such as additional file structures, record access, modification capabilities or automatic transformation of data representations, The File Transfer Access and Management (FTAM) services can be used. The MMS virtual filestore is defined as a subset of the FTAM virtual filestore. The simultaneous access of MMS file services can be achieved via both FTAM and MMS file management services; this is a feature which must be incorporated by the implementor.

## Virtual Terminal Service

The purpose of the virtual terminal service is to allow device independent transactions, thus enabling any terminal to access any computer system on the network. When adopted, the MAP virtual terminal protocol will conform to the ISO model as a layer 7 protocol. No specific protocol recommendation is made at this time.

The virtual terminal protocol will consist of standard message formats to which all terminal data streams are translated for transmission between open systems.

Several different network virtual terminal protocols need to be supported in order to accommodate the different generic types of terminals in use today. Protocols that conform to international or national standards will be used where possible. Some possible classes of service are:

1  Pass-through connection – used in cases where both ends of a connection already expect the same terminal protocol.

2  Character oriented connection – used for character mode asynchronous terminal transactions.

3  Block mode connection – to be used for block mode data entry, line or screen at a time transactions.

4  Graphics mode connection – used for raster graphics terminal oriented transactions.

Classes 2, 3 and 4 will require that the terminal's proprietary protocol and attributes be translated into the MAP virtual terminal protocol at the terminal end of a connection. The computer end of the connection translates the MAP virtual terminal protocol into whatever terminal type the computer application is expecting.

Each of the different classes of service provided by the virtual terminal service meets the needs of a specific range of applications and terminal functions. Currently, Basic, Forms and Graphics classes of service have been identified.

The ISO Basic class service provides a simple character oriented service which meets the terminal access requirements of applications, such as line editing and operating system command language interactions. It will support the types of operations associated with scroll and page mode terminals. It provides the capability to remotely log-on and to run applications remotely in a heterogeneous environment. Used in conjunction with the File Transfer, Access and Management service, it provides third party file transfer capability.

A further addition to the basic service is likely to be a set of 'forms' type functions. This is designed to handle operations associated with block mode terminals.

## MiniMAP, MAP/EPA

MAP 3.0 specifies three functional profiles (sets of options):

1 Peer-to-peer connection oriented profile (PPCOP) constituting the full MAP architecture;

2 Peer-to-peer connectionless profile (PPCLP) miniMAP;

3 Multi-peer connectionless profile (MPCLP) miniMAP allowing the utilisation of multi/broadcast mechanism available on LANs.

All these functional profiles could be implemented into one given end system forming the MAP/EPA architecture. In such a case it is important to permit the possibility of selecting the best profile to be used to satisfy users' service requests with the requested quality of service. This is the function proposed for the MAP profile selector.

The European MAP Users Group regards it essential that:

1 MiniMAP and MAP/EPA provide the portability of eventual migration to a streamlined OSI connectionless profile and should be compatible with the 7-layer model provided the response times remain compatible with critical time applications.

2 Application programs should be given a consistent interface to MAP, MAP/EPA and MiniMAP and should not have to know which one they are using.

Consequently EMUG supports:

1 The introduction of a consistent interface between MiniMAP, MAP/EPA and application programs.

2 The integration of an MMS subset or any other application service element subsets dedicated to critical time applications in the EPA.

The MiniMAP application interface should be a minimum connectionless subset of the application interface specified for the full MAP architecture.

As far as possible, subsets of existing application service elements (MMS, network management, directory services) should be used over the MiniMAP. Private transparent application service element could be used if the required application service is not currently supported by existing application service elements. The application interface should be specified in order to allow such private communication.

As MiniMAP proposes two profiles (PPCLP, MPCLP), a simple profile selection function could optionally be provided. This selection function will allow the selection of either the LLC class 1 or the LLC class 3 service relative to the destination address. In order to do the binding of group address codes received in the destination address field of multicast frames, to application entity titles, it is proposed by EMUG to allow the MiniMAP directory service to contain a separate GROUP ADDRESS_APPLICATION TITLE binding table.

A certain number of functional profiles will be implemented in many end systems, especially at the level of factory mainframes, area managers and cell controllers.

It is proposed to consider the inclusion of a profile selection support function in MAP 3.0 which will aid the user to select the best profile to be used relative to certain criteria.

## Profile Selection

The profile selector is conceptually located in the application interface. When a choice between several profiles is possible the profile selector will select the best profile relative to:

— the respective capabilities of inter-operating end systems;

— the nature of the application service requested by the local users' program;

— the nature of the communications service necessary to execute the application service requested by the local users' program;

— the specified Quality of Service (QOS).

For this purpose the profile selector will provide the following functions:

— establish the respective capabilities of inter-operating end systems;

— select the profile best suited to execute the requested service or set of services with specified QOS;

— check the selected profile is available at the level of inter-operating end systems. In the case of multi-peer profile selection it will be assumed that this condition will be realised;

— in the case of the possible non-availability of the selected profile, identify if an alternative profile is able to execute the requested service or set of services with the specified QOS and if not, return a "profile not available" status to the user's program;

— if the selected profile is available in all inter-operating end systems, identify by means of the directory service the relevant destination address to be used to reach the responding end system. Then establish a link with the local application service access point associated with the selected profile.

The profile selection will be done according to the following four classes of criteria:

— profile availability;

— application service;

— communication service;

— QOS.

**Profile Availability Criteria**

Selection is only possible if the inter-operating peer systems own at least one common functional profile. If several are available in both initiating and responding end systems, it becomes necessary to select the best possible one to be used to satisfy the user's service request with the expected QOS.

**Application Service Criteria**

Profile selection will be done taking into account the following:

— the natural orientation of the application service element;

— the sensitivity of the requested function to current context.

If the application service element is oriented to be supported over a peer-to-peer connection oriented functional profile, such a class profile will be selected relative to availability criteria. If the application service element can be used over any class of profile, the functional profile will be selected relative to:

— profile availability criteria;

— context sensitivity of requested function;

— QOS.

In this latter case:

— for any set of context sensitive functions, selection will be done for the complete set when attaching the user to the service provider. Then the same profile will be used until a detach request is issued;

— for context free functions, the selection can be done on a transaction to transaction basis.

### Communication Service Criteria

It is clear that the communication service derived from the type of the destination address must be provided by the selected profile. Three types of destination address are possible:

— INDIVIDUAL address associated with an AE TITLE;

— GROUP address associated with a group name (group of AEs);

— ALL address associated with all AEs.

A peer-to-peer connectionless profile can only be used if both inter-operating end systems are located on the same LAN segment. In the case of a GROUP or ALL address the multi-peers connectionless profile will be selected.

### Quality Of Service Criteria

QOS Criteria in terms of response time, reliability and security will be used for profile selection. For MAP version 3.0 the selection will be done essentially on urgency criteria. If a request is issued with an 'urgent' indication, peer-to-peer connectionless profile must be selected. If a request is issued with a 'normal' indication, peer-to-peer connection oriented profile will be preferably selected. If the latter is not available in one of the inter-operating end systems, peer-to-peer connectionless profile could be selected as an alternative.

### Call to Profile Selector

When a network function call is passed to the service provider the network function name (service identification) should be accompanied by certain control information, for example:

— destination application entity title or connection identification;

— return event name;

— input parameters;

— output parameters.

Among the input parameters an indication should be given as to whether the user requests the aid of the profile selector. If the user wishes to select a specific profile, this profile must be indicated explicitly. This indication will be accompanied by QOS information. If the user requests the aid of the profile selection support function this is indicated by:

PROFILE SELECTION    SELECTOR

together with QOS information.

## 3.10  APPLICATION INTERFACE

The application layer interface provides the link between the network protocol services and the end users' application programs. The objective of designing the application layer interface is to give the view of a full duplex virtual circuit made available to the application program. The use of a common application interface can offer advantages to both vendors and users:

— It eases portability when moving application programs which make use of MAP networks to a different environment.

— It reduces retraining costs for programmers and support personnel who use the interface in multiple environments.

— It aids the migration of programs into future versions of MAP.

— It promotes third-party application software development for MAP networks.

The MAP application interface interacts with the service provider by calling interface procedures to transfer data between the user and provider. Specific application service providers behave as application programs as far as the MAP service provider is concerned. The provider architecture has 5 key functional units:

1  High-level service provider;

2  Confirmed service provider;

3  Indication filter and arbitrator;

4  Primitive service provider;

5  Protocol machine.

Additionally there is a service provider management function which handles buffering and can enable or disable other functional units.

Both the OSI and EPA application layers need to be supported. These two models are examples of connection oriented and connectionless communication models. The interface should reflect the underlying communication model to the user, but support both models. The prime difference between connection oriented and connectionless communications are:

— The sequence of calls permitted/required;

— The mechanism needed to maintain context.

## Connection Oriented

The usual sequence of calls is:

1   Established association

2   Data transfer

3   Release association

Here there is a context established for an association. In the event of a fault, the association, and thus the context, can be released pending re-instatement of the association. This is the responsibility of both the service user and service provider.

## Connectionless Oriented

### Data Transfer

If each individual data transfer is wholly independent of all other transfers then there is no context to maintain. If the data transfers are not independent of one another, then it is essential to provide context management. This is the responsibility of the service user only.

The application interface design supports two modes of application access, synchronous and asynchronous. Synchronous means that a request is issued and the requester immediately waits for a response before proceeding. Conversely, in an asynchronous function the requester does not wait for a response, but continues processing and is notified later when the request is fully resolved.

To allow an application program to asynchronously interact with network services, a facility to coordinate asynchronously generated events must be provided. Thus, event management is introduced to define a mechanism to notify the requester of the final resolution to an asynchronous event.

## Application Interface Function Classifications

There are three different classification schemes for any application interface function. Each scheme is independent of the others. The three schemes are described below.

## 1 High Level and Low Level

The high-level service provides a user environment where high level functionality is the primary concern. The high-level service does not necessarily provide access to all the functionality of the underlying protocol machine. The typical high-level service function makes use of several low-level service functions to complete its task.

The low-level interface attempts to provide the user with a complete environment where all aspects of the underlying protocol machine capabilities become accessible to the user. This level of interface is useful for protocol testing purposes and is also useful for programmers who want to have a tight control over all interactions with the underlying protocol machine.

## 2 Requester and Responder Mode

The requester mode functions give a user the ability to request services of a network. Such a mode of operation is most typical with FTAM application functions.

The responder mode functions exist at the other end of a request. These functions set up mechanisms to automatically respond to requester mode functions issued by a peer application. The MMS interface requires such functions.

## 3 Context Free and Context Sensitive

A context free function can be issued as a stand-alone function with no established context. The issue of such a function is not influenced by network functions issued before it nor does it affect any functions issued after it. As an example, the File Copy function defined in the FTAM Application Interface Specification is a context-free function.

A context-sensitive call is the exact opposite of a context-free call. Whether one should issue such a call depends largely on the context established by previous network function calls. Functions that operate on a particular application association are context sensitive.

### Application Interface Architecture

The application interface model is divided into two parts, the set of services which are part of the user program, and the service provider, which can be viewed as a separate process. Both the set of services and the service providers are organised into functional blocks. The general nature of the function of each functional block is described below.

### High-Level Service

The set of grouped services (either context sensitive or context free) available to the application process.

### Low Level Service

The set of service primitives available in the application process.

### Responder Service

The set of services which will automatically screen incoming unsolicited service indications and determine a particular course of action.

### Service Provider

The services available from the service provider are provided by a task which is not part of the application process. Each service provider function block is an entity in itself. The user can repeatedly request service from a particular function block. An implementation is required to ensure the orderly processing of all multiple outstanding requests.

### Application Interface Support Functions

There are currently four areas for which support functions have been defined: event management, dynamic data control block allocation, translation of returned error codes to printable strings, and notification that a resource constraint has cleared.

## Event Management

The event management system (EM) provides services allowing events to be defined, noted and awaited. The objectives of event management are:

— To be able to write event-driven programs and to be able to handle multiple connections within a single process. EM allows a user to wait on one or more multiple events, with an event defined as the completion of an operation started via an asynchronous function call.

— To provide a consistent interface across different services. EM is used by all user interfaces, so it can be very desirable to have its interface change as little as possible as it is implemented in various systems. The most direct method of ensuring such compatibility across systems is to explicitly specify the requisite event management functionality.

— To minimise assumptions concerning operating systems support. Assumptions about what types of operating systems support need to be available are minimised, since the only requirement is that a process be able to be deactivated and activated by whatever means are available on the particular operating system.

— To not preclude the use of the same mechanism for non-MAP events. This could allow the writing of event-driven programs which have functions other than communications.

Event management is felt not to offer sufficient to warrant implementation in:

— environments that have no real ability to handle asynchronous events;

— environments that have substantially better facilities for handling asynchronous events.

## Usage Scenario for Event Management

The routines using event management, ie the routines which either wait on events or note the occurence of events, must come to some agreement on what unambiguous names to give the particular events they use. This can be done in various ways; for instance, by prior agreement, by generating names according to an algorithm, or by having one program generate names which it then passes to the other programs needing the names. EM does not specify how to generate or agree on event names, but once agreement is reached it does need to be informed of which names are to be used. This is accomplished by having each asynchronous application interface function specify an event name representing its completion.

The program which implements the function then uses the event name to note a specific occurance of the event.

### Connection Management Interface

This section on the connection management interface provides a definition for the Association Control Service Elements (ACSE) and is one part of a complete application interface specification. It is used in conjunction with other connection oriented application layer service interface specifications, such as File Transfer Access and Management interface and Manufacturing Message Service interface.

Within the application layer, an Application Entity (AE) is the only object which can be addressed in an OSI environment. The actual performance of the functions of an AE must be carried out by an AE invocation.

### Application Entity Registration

In order than an application entity utilises the services of the application interface, the following must be carried out:

— For each Application Entity (AE) a fully qualified Presentation address must be assigned.

— Normally, each AE title will be registered with the network directory. However, it is entirely possible to have an AE that does not want to be known to the network community. It is also possible for an AE to have no title. In such cases, the AE is not registered with the network wide directory.

— Specifications related to the characteristics of the AE which must be known to the management are provided. The information is not expected to change during run-time for an AE invocation.

### ACSE Interactions With Other ASEs

Whenever an association request is issued, a particular application context must be selected in order to make the association meaningful.

The functions provided by an ASE association request function are:

— to check the legitimacy of the ASE specific information presented by the user;

— if the information is legitimate, to generate an ASE specific Initiate APDU and generate A_ASSOCIATE parameters required by the ACSE.

The functions provided by an ACSE association request function are:

— to check the legitimacy of the ACSE information presented by the user;

— if the information is legitimate and the ASE has approved the request, then to generate the A_ASSOCIATE request to the ACSE protocol machine.

As soon as a response to an association request Protocol Data Unit (PDU) is detected, the corresponding ASE will be informed. The ASE assocation response function must present ASE specific response information to the user. The ACSE association response function must present the rest of the response information to the user.

The information required from the application service elements is notification of:

— application entity activation;

— connection establishment;

— connection release;

— connection abort;

— error diagnostics.

This information denotes the phases of action for which the connection management is responsible.

**Private Communications Application Interface**

The services that make up the Private Communications interface are intended to provide easy access to the facilities required to establish an association using 'PRIVATE' (Private Communication) application context and to transfer data within this context. The capabilities provided by this service are based on the MAP presentation layer services.

The PRIVATE COMMUNICATIONS Application Interface Definition is designed to support communications between two application entities that have agreed to exchange information via the MAP defined 'PRIVATE' context.

In order to participate in such a conversation, an application entity must first be activated using the AE activation service provided by the connection management. Once activated, an AE may attempt to establish associations with other AEs by using the connection service provided by the connection management, and by specifying that the 'PRIVATE' application context is to be used.

Since the primary goal of the PRIVATE COMMUNICATIONS Applications Interface is to support the peer-to-peer exchange of user data, a key role of this interface is to accept data from the user and pass it on to the network service provider.

### FTAM Application Interface

This interface provides the user with the capability of accessing various File Transfer Access and Management functions. There are two levels of service provided in this interface: context-free and context-sensitive services.

Context-free services provide a high-level service which results in the exchange of several FTAM primitives. No special knowledge of FTAM protocol is required to use these services. They provide a complete, autonomous action on the specific filestores. An example of a context-free type service is the file copy. This interface provides the capability of copying a file from one filestore to another filestore with no additional FTAM protocol interaction.

Context-sensitive services are more primitive in nature and require a knowledge of FTAM protocols.

Control of FTAM assocation is through the standard connection management facilities defined for the application interface.

The following section describes the function of the FTAM services available to the FTAM user.

### 1   Context Free Functions

#### i   File Copy

The file copy service allows a file to be copied between any two filestores on the network. If the copy is successful the file will exist in an identical form in both filestores.

## ii  File Move

The file move service allows a file to be moved between any two filestores on the network. If the move is successful, after the file is moved the source file is deleted from the source filestore.

## iii  File Delete

The file delete service allows a file to be removed from any filestore on the network. If the delete service is successful, the file will not exist after the delete service completes.

## iv  File Read Attributes

The file read attributes service allows the user to read the values of any attributes, except passwords, of any file in any filestore on the network. The result of a successful completion of the file read attributes service is to return to the user the values of the attributes requested.

## v  File Change Attributes

The file change attributes service allows the user to modify the values of any filename, storage account, file availability, future file size, access control, legal qualifications or private use file attributes of any file in any filestore on the network. If the file change attributes service is successful, all of the attributes specified for change will have the value specified for that attribute and all attributes not specified for change will have the same value as before the file change attributes service was invoked.

The file copy, file move, file delete, file read attributes and file change attributes are all context-free services belonging to the set of services called high level services; the actual service is provided by the high level service provider.

## 2  Context Sensitive Functions

## i  File Open

The file open service allows the user to open a file for access to its content. The file may be any file in the filestore to which a connection has been established. The file does not need to exist before the invocation of the file open service. The service user may specify what action, if any, to take if the file exists before the invocation of the file open service. If the file open is successful, the file will be available for access through the use of the set of file access services (read, write, locate, erase) except where limited by service agreements made between the service users, or by the file access agreements made between the service users.

## ii  File Close

The file close service allows the user to stop access to a file's contents previously permitted by a file open service. The file closed is the one most recently opened on the specified connection. The service user may specify whether the file is to remain in the filestore or be deleted from it by the file close service. After completion of the file close service, the file will no longer be available for access through the use of any of the file access services (read, write, locate, erase).

## iii  Reset

The reset service allows the user to rewind the file to the beginning of the file. The file which is rewound is the file most recently opened in the filestore specified by the connection identifier. If the reset service is successful, the file marker will be positioned at the beginning of the file.

## iv  Seek

The seek service allows the user to locate a specified position within the file. The file which is referenced is the file most recently opened in the filestore specified by the connection identifier. If the seek service is successful, the file will be positioned where specified.

## v  Extend

The extend service allows the user to position at the end of a file. The file which is referenced is the file most recently opened in the filestore specified by the connection identifier. If the extend service is successful the file marker will be positioned at the end of the file.

The file open, file close, reset, seek and extend are all context-sensitive services belonging to the set of services called high-level services; the actual service provided by the high-level service provider.

## vi  Select

The select service is used to make a file available for access in the filestore to which a connection was previously established. If the specified file does not exist then the select service fails. If the select service is successful, the specified file will be in the same state as before the invocation of the select service and will be available for subsequent access.

## vii  De-select

The de-select service is used to end the access to a file previously selected in the filestore to which a connection was previously established. If the de-select service is successful, the specified file will be in the same state (file contents and attributes may be changed) as before the invocation of the select service and will no longer be available for access unless subsequently selected.

## viii  Open

The open service is used to make the previously selected file available for access to its contents in the filestore to which a connection was previously established. If the open service is successful, the specified file will be in the same state as before the invocation of the open service and will be available for subsequent access to its contents.

## ix  Close

The close service is used to make the previously opened file unavailable for access to its contents in the filestore to which a connection was previously established. If the close service is successful, the file will be in the same state as before the invocation of the close service and will not be available for subsequent access to its contents.

## x  Create

The create service generally causes a file to be created and selected in the filestore to which a connection was previously established. If the specified file already exists, then depending on the value of the file-status parameter, the action would be one of the following:

— create service fails – the existing file is unchanged;

— select the existing file – the existing file is unchanged;

— delete the contents (but not the attributes) of the file and select the file;

— delete the existing file and create a new file using the attribute values specified in the Attribute-Value parameter.

If the create service is successful, the state of the file is as specified above.

*xi   Delete*

The delete service deletes the currently selected file from the filestore to which a connection was previously established. If the delete service is successful, the file will no longer exist in the filestore and the file will not be available for subsequent access.

*xii   Read Attribute*

The read attribute service is used to read the values of the attributes of the previously selected file in the filestore to which a connection was previously established. If the read attribute service is succesful, the state of the file is the same as before the read attribute service was invoked and the values of the attributes requested will be returned (if available) in the output data area.

*xiii   Change Attribute*

The change attribute service is used to modify the values of the attributes of the previously selected file in the filestore to which a connection was previously established. If the change attribute service is successful, the state of the file is the same as before the change attribute service was invoked except for the changed attribute values.

*xiv   Read*

The read service is used to request the transfer from the filestore for part, or all, of the contents of the previously opened file in the filestore to which a connection was previously established. The identity parameter identifies which part of the file will be transferred. If the read service is not successful, the state of the file is the same as before the read service was invoked and the request will be made of the filestore.

*xv   Write*

The write service is used to request the transfer to the filestore of data to be placed into the previously opened file in the filestore to which a connection was previously established. The operation parameter identifies the specific write action which is to take place. This parameter may take the value 'insert', 'replace' or 'extend'. The identity parameter identifies where in the file contents the write action is to take place. If the write action is successful, the state of the file is the same as before the write service was invoked (the file contents may subsequently be modified when data is transferred) and the request will be made of the filestore.

*xvi   Erase*

The erase service is used to remove from the file part, or all, of the contents of the previously opened file in the filestore to which a connection was established. The portion of the file contents to be removed from the file is specified by the identity parameter. If the erase service is successful, the state of the file is the same as before the erase service was invoked, except that the specified portion of the file contents have been removed from the file and the position of the file pointer within the file contents may be changed.

*xvii   Locate*

The locate service is used to move a pointer to the specified place in the file contents of the previously opened file in the filestore to which a connection was previously established. The pointer may be used as a reference for subsequent read, write, erase or locate service invocations. If the locate service is successful, the state of the file is the same as before the locate service was invoked and the pointer will be moved to the specified point in the file contents.

*xviii   Send Data*

The send data service is used to transfer a block of data to the previously opened file in the filestore to which a connection was previously established. The filestore will write the data transferred to the file as specified in the previous write service invocation. If the send data service is successful, the state of the file is unknown, but the data will have been sent to the filestore to be written to the file as specified with the previous write service invocation.

*xix   Receive Data*

The receive data service is used to get a block of data which has been transferred from the previously opened file in the filestore to which a connection was previously established. If the receive data is successful, the data will have been placed in the data buffer provided.

The end of the data transfer is indicated by receipt of a DATA END indication or CANCEL indication primitive. When either a DATA END or a CANCEL request PDU is received, the corresponding DATA END indication primitive will be passed to the service user as the data in the data buffer.

*xx   Data End*

The data end service is used to indicate the end of a sequence of send data service invocations and marks the end of the data being transferred to the previously opened file in the filestore to which a connection was previously established. If the data end service is successful, the data end request PDU will have been sent to the filestore and the data stream terminated.

### xxi   Transfer End

The transfer end service is used to indicate the end of the data transfer phase for the previously opened file in the filestore to which a connection was previously established. If the transfer end service is successful, the data transfer phase will have been ended and the state of the file will be the same as before the read or write service was invoked, except that the position of the pointer within the file contents may be changed and the contents of the file may have been changed if the write service was previously invoked.

### xxii   Begin Group

The begin group service allows the user to designate the beginning of a series of primitive requests to be treated by the FTAM protocol machine as one presentation service data unit. If the begin group request is successful, subsequent service requests will be included in the group until such time that the end group service is invoked.

The Return_Event_Name parameter may not specify that the service is to be performed as a synchronous service. Invocation of the begin group service restricts all subsequent service invocations up to the next invocation of the end group service such that the Return_Event_Name of each of the services may not specify that the service is to be performed as a synchronous service.

### xxiii   End Group

The end group service allows the user to designate the end of the series of primitive requests to be treated by the FTAM protocol machine as one presentation service data unit. If the end group request is successful, previous service invocation will be included in the group and sent to the responding machine.

Successful completion of the end group service removes the restrictions on the Return_Event_Name parameter value placed on service invocations by the invocation of the begin group service primitive.

### xxiv   Cancel Request

The cancel service allows the user to end the data transfer in progress to or from the filestore to which a connection was previously established. If the cancel service is successful, the data transfer phase will have been ended and if data was being written to the file the state of the file will be determined by the data received by the filestore prior to receiving the cancel indication and local filestore considerations.

*xxv    Cancel Response*

The cancel response service allows the user to acknowledge the end of the data transfer in progress to or from the filestore to which a connection was previously established. If the cancel response service is successful, the data transfer phase will have been ended and if data was being written to the file the state of the file will be determined by the data received by the filestore prior to issuing the cancel request and local filestore considerations.

The select, deselect, open, close, create, delete, read attribute, change attribute, read, write, erase, locate, send data, receive data, data end, transfer end, begin group, end group, cancel request and cancel response are all context-free services belonging to the set of services called low-level services; the actual service is provided by the primitive service provider.

If any of the FTAM services are not successful the files should not be altered. Specific areas to address when considering the application programmer's needs are:

—    transportability of code;

—    ease of learning and use;

—    good development environment;

—    run-time efficiency.

In considering the needs of the supplier of a MAP environment, issues to address include:

—    compatibility with existing architecture;

—    ease of enhancement;

—    conformance testing;

—    user satisfaction.

**MMS Application Interface**

The Manufacturing Message Service interface is the interface between the MMS user and the MMS Application Service Element (ASE). The MMS interface has both context-free and context-sensitive functions. Most of the functions are context sensitive, in the sense that an association must have been established previously by using the context management services. The user of the MMS interface is an Application Process (AP). An AP can make use of other application service elements as well as MMS.

The following section describes the function of the MMS services available to the MMS user.

## 1   Context Sensitive Functions

### i   *Identify*

The identify function allows identifying information to be retrieved from the peer application process.

### ii   *Cancel*

The cancel service is used by an MMS user to cancel a request that has previously been issued, but has not yet been completed.

### iii   *Get Name List*

The get name list service is used by an MMS user to obtain a list of names which are known to the remote MMS responder. This list of names may be accessed one at a time by the support function Interpret Name List.

### iv   *Indication Receive*

There are two responses to the Indication Receive function. These are:

   a   Reject Indication

A master application may receive reject indications from the MMS server. This is done by calling the Indication Receive funtion, whose outputs may indicate a reject indication was received.

   b   Unsolicited Status Indication

The MMS interface specification is intended for master applications. Such applications do not give their status, in general (at least not via the MMS unsolicited status indication, which is meant for slave applications). On the other hand a master application can expect to receive unsolicited status indications from slave applications (such as numerical controllers and programmable controllers). This is achieved by calling the Indication Receive function, waiting for the data, and then calling the status report function to interpret the status data.

## v  Status

The purpose of the status function is to determine the general condition of a responding entity and optionally obtain additional detail.

## vi  Start

The start service is used by an MMS user to initiate control activity at a control device. The use of this service for a particular type of equipment is to be defined by other standards bodies for individual applications.

## vii  Stop

The stop service is used by an MMS user to suspend control activity at a control device. The use of this service for a particular type of equipment is to be defined by other standards bodies for individual applications.

## viii  File Functions

### a  Load from File

The purpose of the load from file function is to have a specified file loaded at a remote application process, either as an executable program or as data in a network variable.

### b  Store to File

The purpose of the store to file function is to store a loaded program or network variable to a specified file.

### c  File Get

The purpose of the file get function is to effect a file transfer from the peer application process to the local application process. It is a grouped function which invokes three MMS service primitives: file-open-request, file-read-request and file-close-request.

### d  File Put

The purpose of the file put function is to effect a file transfer from the local user application process to a remote application process. It is also possible to substitute a third-party application process for the local user application process, resulting in a file transfer from one remote application process to another.

### e   File Rename

The purpose of the file rename function is to rename a file at a remote application process.

### f   File Delete

The purpose of the file delete function is to delete a file at a remote application process.

### g   File Directory

The purpose of the file directory function is to obtain directory information on a particular file or set of files from a remote application process.

### h   File Upload

The purpose of the file upload function is to transfer an executable program, that exists in a ready-to-execute state on the responding user, from the responding user to the specified file on the requesting user's filestore. It is a grouped function which invokes three MMS service primitives: initiate-upload-sequence, receive-upload-segment, and terminate-upload-sequence.

### i   File Download

The purpose of the file download function is to transfer an executable program from the filestore of the requesting user to the executable program space of the responding user. This function is a grouped function which invokes three MMS service primitives: initiate-download-sequence, receive-download-segment, and terminate-download-sequence.

## ix   Memory Functions

### a   Initiate Memory Download

The purpose of the initiate memory download function is to allow the requesting user to instruct the responding user to prepare to receive a program of a specified name for loading into the specified loading configuration. The initiate memory download function is a paired function which invokes the MMS initiate-download-sequence service primitive and waits for the confirmation. The function is used in conjunction with the transmit memory download and terminate memory download functions. These functions together have the same effect as the single file-download function, except that the download image originates in the requester's memory, not his file store.

b   Transmit Memory Download

The purpose of the transmit memory download function is to transfer a segment of an executable program from the designated memory area on the requesting user to the load configuration identified on the responding user by a preceding call to the initiate memory download function. The transmit memory download function is a paired function and invokes the transmit-download-segment MMS service primitives and handles the confirmation.

c   Terminate Memory Download

The purpose of the terminate memory download function is to permit the requesting user to indicate to the responding user that the download transaction is complete. The terminate memory download function is a paired function which invokes the MMS terminate-download-sequence service primitive, and handles the confirmation.

d   Initiate Memory Upload

The purpose of the initiate memory upload function is to allow the requesting user to instruct the responding user to prepare to upload the program of the specified name. This function is a paired function which invokes the MMS initiate-upload-sequence service primitive, and waits for the confirmation.

e   Transmit Memory Upload

The purpose of the transmit memory upload function is to transfer a segment of an executable program, which exists in a ready-to-execute state on the responding user, from the responding user to the designated memory area of the requesting user. The transmit memory upload function is a paired function which invokes the receive-upload-segment MMS service primitives and handles the confirmation.

### f  Terminate Memory Upload

The purpose of the terminate memory upload function is to transfer an executable program, which exists in a ready-to-execute state on the responding user, from the responding user to a specified memory location on the requesting user. The terminate memory upload function is a paired function which invokes the MMS terminate-upload-sequence service primitives, and handles the confirmation.

### x  Semaphore Functions

#### a  Take Semaphore Control

The purpose of the take semaphore control function is to take control of a semaphore (resource) either locally or at a remote application process.

#### b  Relinquish Semaphore Control

The purpose of the relinquish semaphore control function is to relinquish control of a semaphore or resource locally or at a remote application process.

#### c  Semaphore Define

The purpose of the semaphore define function is to define a new semaphore either locally or at a remote application process.

#### d  Semaphore Delete

The purpose of the semaphore delete function is to delete an existing semaphore either locally or at a remote application process.

#### e  Semaphore Status Report

The purpose of the semaphore status report function is to obtain the status of a particular semaphore or resource from a remote application process or from the local system.

### xi  Functions on Variables

#### a  Read Variable

The purpose of the read variable function is to effect the reading of one or more variables from the peer application process. If the operation is successful, the resulting data or a pointer for the resulting data (known as a 'handle') is returned as an output parameter.

## b Write Variable

The purpose of this function is to effect the writing of data into one or more variables in the peer application process. The success or failure of the operation is returned in the output parameter return-code.

## c Information Report

The purpose of this function is to effect the sending of unsolicited information, or for sending the values of variables specified in a previously received program event action message.

## d Information Report Indication

A master application can expect to receive information report indications from slave applications (such as robots, numerical controllers and programmable controllers), or from other master applications. This is done by calling the indication-receive-function, waiting for the data, and then calling the extract-list-element-function and/or one or more 'interpret' functions.

## e Define Variable Name

The purpose of the define variable name function is to effect the defining of a variable name in the peer application process and associate it with a specific variable specification, so that the name may be used in subsequent service requests.

## f Get Variable Name Definition

The purpose of the get variable name definition function is to effect the obtaining of the definition of a specified variable name in the peer application process.

## g Delete Variable Name

The purpose of the delete variable name function is to effect the deleting of the definition of a specified variable name in the peer application process.

*xii   Type Name Functions*

    a   Define Type Name

The purpose of the define type name is to effect the defining of the type name to associate with the specified type description in the peer application process.

    b   Get Type Name Definition

The purpose of the get type name definition function is to effect the obtaining of the type description associated with a type name from the peer application process.

    c   Delete Type Name

The purpose of the delete type name function is to effect the deletion of the type description associated with a type name from the peer application process.

## 2   Context Free Functions

*i   Make List*

The purpose of the make list function is to either append an element to an existing list of similar elements, or to create a new list consisting of a single element.

*ii   New Restriction*

The purpose of the new restriction function is to create a restriction definition within the interface for future use in a partial-access definition.

*iii   New Partial Access*

The purpose of the new partial access function is to create a new partial access definition within the interface for future use in a type description or a variable access definition.

*iv   New MMS Type*

The purpose of the new MMS type function is to create a new MMS type definition within the interface for future use.

*v   New Structure Component*

The purpose of the new structure component function is to create a new structure component definition within the interface for future use in creating a type description for structure types.

*vi   New Variable Access*

The purpose of the new variable access function is to create a new variable access specification within the interface for future use in creating a variable association.

*vii   New Variable Association*

The purpose of the new variable association function is to create a new variable association within the interface for future use in read, write, define variable and information report functions. A variable association consist of one or more of the following pieces of information:

1   Name of the association.

2   Specification of the variable to be defined or accessed.

3   Type description of the variable to be defined or accessed.

4   Address of local memory which is going to be the source/destination of the data or the 'handle' to data representation to be written/read to/ from the peer application process.

Not all of these pieces are always relevant. For example, in define-variable-service, only the variable specification is required, while in read-variable, both variable specification, type and address of local memory are relevant. For this purpose, a parameter is used which specifies whether the association is variable-only (only variable specification information) or data-only (only data information) or variable-data (both variable specification and data information).

*viii   New Data*

The purpose of the new data function is to create a new data representation within the interface for future use.

*ix   Interpretation Functions*

    a   Interpret Restriction

    The purpose of the interpret restriction function is to interpret the definition of a restriction within the interface. This function is symmetric to the new-restriction function.

### b   Extract List Element

The purpose of the extract list element function is to extract an element from a list.

### c   Interpret Partial Access

The purpose of the interpret partial access function is to interpret a partial access definition within the interface.

### d   Interpret MMS Type

The purpose of the interpret MMS type function is to interpret the information in a handle of type MMS-type. This is symmetric to the function new-MMS-type.

### e   Interpret Structure Component

The purpose of the interpret structure component is to interpret the information in a structure component definition.

### f   Interpret Variable Access

The purpose of the interpret variable access function is to interpret the information in a variable access specification handle.

### g   Interpret Variable Association

The purpose of the interpret variable association function is to interpret the information in a variable association definition within the interface. A variable association consists of one or more of the following pieces of information: name of the association, specification of the variable to be defined or accessed, type description of the variable to be defined or accessed, address of local memory which is going to be the source/ destination of the data to be written/read in to/from the peer application process.

### h   Interpret Data Representation

The purpose of the interpret data representation function is to extract information/data from the internal representation of data within the interface.

### i   Duplicate Handle

The purpose of the duplicate handle function is to make a logical copy of an object referenced by a handle so that it can be used again.

### j   Free Handle

The purpose of the free handle function is to explicitly free the logical copy of the object referenced by a handle which is no longer required.

### k   Interpret Status Response

The purpose of the interpret status response function is to interpret the information in a status confirmation or in an unsolicited status indication.

### l   Interpret Configuration

The configuration information that is contained in the identify-confirmation can be accessed through the interpret configuration function. Each call returns configuration data on a different subsystem until the function's return value indicates there is no more configuration data. It can later be re-accessed by resetting the position parameter to zero. The interpret configuration function operates synchronously on local user data.

### m   Interpret Name List

The name-list parameter of the get-name-list function, described in the section on context sensitive functions, can be accessed through the interpret name list function. Each call returns another name until the functions return value indicates there are no more names. It can later be re-accessed by resetting the position parameter to zero. The interpret name list function operates synchronously on local user data.

### n   Interpret File Directory

The file directory function call, described in the context sensitive functions, returns an arbitrary list of file directory entries of variable length, which can be accessed via the interpret file directory function. Each call of this function returns the information of a different file directory entry until the function's return value indicates there is no more data. The list can later be re-accessed by resetting the position parameter to zero. The interpret file directory function operates synchronously on local user data.

o   Interpret Application Entity Titles

The semaphore status report function call, described in the context sensitive functions, returns an arbitrary list of application entity (AE) titles of varying length which can be accessed by the interpret application entity titles function. Each call of the function returns a different AE title until the function's return value indicates there is no more data. The list can later be re-accessed by resetting the position parameter to zero. The interpret AE titles function operates synchronously on user data.

## MMS in the EPA Environment

To the end user, MMS is used in the EPA environment in a manner similar to its use in the full MAP environment except that:

1   The MMS user's interface to the MMS provider must provide a mechanism for the MMS user to specify whether a given message is to be sent using the services of the seven-layer side of the EPA or the services of the three-layer side. Likewise, the MMS provider must indicate which side of the EPA was used for incoming communications. This mechanism may be part of the manner in which the identification of the remote peer MMS user is passed between the local MMS user and the MMS provider.

2   The manner in which the MMS user specifies the name and/or address of the remote peer may be different for the three-layer side of the EPA in comparison to the seven-layer side of the EPA and the full MAP communications. The local user may use the MiniMAP object dictionary to acquire the address of the remote peer.

3   There are some additional MMS service primitives used when communicating on the three-layer side of the EPA. Depending on the urgency of the communication the MMS user may need to be able to issue and/or receive these primitives.

4   The option of selecting connectionless or connection-oriented communication exists when using the three-layer side of the EPA. The full MAP services do not support associationless operation. Since

associationless operation is supported on the three-layer side, multi-cast transmission of unconfirmed MMS request protocol data units is also supported.

5   The set of MMS services available using the three-layer side of the EPA in associationless mode is more restricted than the set available in association-oriented communications, using either seven layers or three layers.

The use of the full seven-layer side of the EPA is the same as the use of EPA in the full MAP environment, except that the user may have to specify that the seven-layer side is being used.

The set of services available when using the three-layer side of the EPA is determined by whether the connection-oriented or connectionless mode is used. The use of connection-oriented mode means the available set of MMS services is exactly the same as specified in MMS in the full MAP environment. There are message size limitations when communication over the three side EPA node is used. These size restrictions may limit the functionality of the MMS services. A limited set of services is available for connectionless mode.

## Service Interface

The interface to the services is defined in terms of service primitives and protocols, comprising calling sequences and data structures and values. An application with access to the service is not presently available. For the future, the primitives alone could be offered; a confirmed service to call paired primitives might be available; or a service to invoke a larger group of related primitives could be provided.

In addition it is necessary to provide supporting services; eg buffer allocation.

## EPA Application

When an application interfaces to a MiniMAP architecture several functions otherwise provided by the full architecture may optionally need to be performed by the application.

## 3.11   MAP/EPA

The MAP specification was originally created to allow manufacturing computers to communicate data without regard to the operating system or computer manufacturer. Process control users felt the need for a subset of MAP services that would sacrifice some functionality to achieve faster messaging response times. The modified architecture agreed for time critical applications allows certain layers of the OSI reference model used in the MAP specification to be optionally bypassed to increase localised responsiveness. The result of this is the Enhanced Performance Architecture.

## User Requirements

The control systems network is required to provide:

— rapid response for short high-priority messages;

— high reliability of the media and signalling method, even in very harsh environments, providing a very low bit error rate and minimum number of retransmissions;

— a network maintainable and modifiable by maintenance personnel;

— a network that can assign lower priorities to any traffic not required for the main control functions;

— a network that can easily connect (either through a bridge or router) to the main data network;

— a network that can maintain some access security to prevent unauthorised connection from outside users;

— a network that supports methods for redundancy for network components to maintain high reliability;

— a network that may require very little or no support from directory servers to carry out its function. This function may be programmed or provided by a simplified subset of the main directory service which is locally maintained.

Two examples of the areas where such networks are required are manufacturing cells and process control systems.

A *manufacturing cell* is a group of machines which are linked together to perform specific tasks. To distribute the work amongst a diverse array of machines such as these requires a network that is simple, relatively inexpensive, and usable by a variety of devices. The network should also be easily rearranged and reconfigured since cells can be expanded, modified or relocated, depending on the needs of the plant. Most of the traffic within the cell (70-95%) will involve local communication only, ie between cell members, although the cell may also have to communicate with devices outside it.

Many industries require distributed control of several different processes. These processes are controlled by many different devices which often need to communicate with each other to automate their process effectively. These *process control* systems typically require rapid network response time in order to effectively distribute the control functions of the process they are controlling.

Nodes on time critical networks may require a response to an inquiry in less than one token rotation of the network. To achieve this response immediate acknowledge services are required. These services will allow for a node to receive message delivery acknowledgements or data replies from a remote node while the local node still holds the token. This service also provides for immediate retry if data or an acknowledgement is not received in a timely manner, and for local reporting of message delivery failure in the event that no acknowledgement or data is received after the retry counters have expired.

It is often necessary in manufacturing and control networks to provide redundancy for certain critical components and systems. The problem of redundant cable implementations due to cable breaks and cable degradation is one of the most common network problems in factory environments. EPA will support work carried out in this area when it is included in the MAP specification.

Using EPA means that some services provided by the full architecture are sacrificed. The following services provided by the MAP OSI layers are not available:

— **High Quality Guaranteed Message Delivery**   The EPA services do not guarantee delivery of messages, but they do ensure that an attempt will be made to deliver a message and receive an acknowledgement and that failure to acknowledge delivery of a message will be made known to the service user.

— **Global Delivery of Messages**   EPA services cannot be used for acknowledged delivery of messages outside the local segment.

— **Indefinite Message Length**   Message size is limited when using the EPA services to the maximum data link unit size.

— **Session Services**   Since there is no session layer the ability to resynchronise dialogues between applications or provide checkpoints is lost.

— **Presentation Services**   The presentation syntax must be known in advance for applications that use the EPA services. The ability to negotiate or change abstract syntax encoding during an application association is not available.

— **Full Flow Control**   Applications that use EPA services will only be able to maintain one outstanding (unacknowledged) message at a time, which may reduce throughput.

— **Concept of Connection**   The EPA services are connectionless only.

The MAP/EPA architecture is compatible with the full MAP architecture at layers 1 and 2 and shares some of the application packages at layer 7. There is a direct application to data link interface.

Devices may exist that will contain the EPA side of the MAP/EPA architecture but will not contain the full 7 layer MAP architecture. These nodes are not OSI compatible and cannot communicate outside their local segment without a gateway. Devices based on the full 7 layer model which are required to use a time critical link service and any functionality such as file transfer, full MAP directory services or the ability to communicate with other segments should contain the dual MAP/EPA architecture.

EPA segments may be connected to other LANs by three different interconnecting devices; bridges, routers and gateways.

The MAP/EPA architecture is designed for networks that require very fast response times for time-critical applications. Care should be taken, however, not to use a reduced layer structure if the functionality of the missing layers is required. It will only result in trying to add this in to the application layer (and above)!

*Network Management*

Network management in communications is not a new concept. The requirements which network management had to fill for the MAP specification are as follows:

— to provide tools putting as few constraints on MAP products as possible;

— to assist each system in its own management as conceptually network management is distributed over the network;

— to trade off distributed application support in favour of 'end' system simplicity;

— to drive network management standards where they are not available in order to achieve widespread support;

— to ensure that network management activities occur infrequently and on an exception basis (this prevents the network being flooded with irrelevant information);

— to ensure that isolated failures do not affect the network manager's operation;

— to ensure that a path of upwards compatibility is provided by recognising the evolution of networking facilities;

— to recognise the need for implementation specific extensions to the management facilities.

In essence network management has the responsibility for gathering information on the usage of the network media by the network devices themselves, ensuring the correct operation of the network and providing relevant reports in an acceptable format. The various types of information which are collected is processed to be used for planning operations or maintenance. To the outside world the network management architecture is based on three components which gather and process these various types of information, these are:

— network manager application; providing the mechanism for the network administrator to read or alter data, control a network and accessory ports;

— manager-agent protocol; responsible for collecting management information from the various layers on a specific node (this being system dependent) and to exchange the management information collected from its own local system with another systems management application process (SMAP) on a remote node;

— management information base; comprising a set of management data in an open system available to the network manager application using the manager agent protocol.

Further details of these are available in the MAP specification.

Fibre optic transmission systems have taken a substantially higher profile in the MAP specification. The transmission method is based on that of light pulses propagating down fibres. The technology, although new, and in the past expensive, is now becoming more recognised and more achievable and, in addition, has distinct advantages over other transmission media. These advantages relate to:

— noise immunity;

— safety;

— high data rates;

— security;

— isolation.

In addition, they are low in weight and have attenuation independent of the data rate as well as being able to cover long distances. The trend towards the use of optical fibre is increasing mainly from a progressive understanding of the technology through its acceptance resulting in increased sales of systems and hence lower cost to the end user. Like any technology it demands understanding and support and in this respect can be likened to the difference between supporting a baseband network compared with supporting a broadband network. It inherently requires the user to fully understand the implications of taking on board fibre optic technology within his plans.

This chapter has explained some salient points within the MAP specification and, where necessary, made comparisons between version 2.1 and 3.0. Version 3.0 of the MAP specification is now said to be stable for a few years in order that suppliers and users alike can take advantage of the work that has been done. Having defined the MAP architecture (Chapter 2) and the MAP specification (this chapter), the next chapter explains some of the products and systems which are currently available and which make use of this architecture and specification.

# Part 2

# MAP — The Practice

# 4 Products and Systems

## 4.1 INTRODUCTION

Although it is somewhat dangerous to talk about products and systems which are currently on the market for the support of MAP version 3.0, because such information will quickly become dated, a saving factor is that MAP version 3.0 will now be stable for a period of time. The products and systems considered in this chapter should be used as reference. There is no substitute for keeping close contact with the suppliers in order to gain information relating to their direction and provision of systems and products.

The inclusion or exclusion within this chapter of any manufacturers' systems should not be viewed as an endorsement or indeed lack of faith in the relevant supplier. What the chapter does provide is a snapshot of the products and systems which were available at the time of publication and which illustrate the point of putting the theory of the previous two chapters into practice.

The previous chapters have described the ISO model, upon which MAP is based, the MAP architecture and the MAP specification – in essence the theory. The remaining chapters put the theory into practice and are in keeping with the theme of the book. MAP has been frozen at version 3.0 with the intention of giving suppliers the chance to develop products and systems. The ones contained in this section are 'snapshots' of those currently available and any inclusion or omission is not meant to imply recommendation or otherwise. The products and systems described here, however, do provide the opportunity (as previously pointed out) to illustrate relevant teaching points.

## 4.2 RACAL-MILGO AND CONCORD COMMUNICATIONS INCORPORATED

Racal-Milgo is the sole distributor in the UK for Concord Communications' Token/Net (Concord Communications Incorporated is a subsidary of Concord

Data Systems, dedicated to MAP-compatible networks). Token/Net was the first local area network to comply with the IEEE 802.4 standard for broadband token bus LANs, as well as with the MAP standards for communications in a manufacturing environment. Token/Net provides the ability to link various kinds of digital devices – including data processing systems, CAD/CAM (Computer Aided Design/Computer Aided Manufacture) workstations and robots – on the factory floor. A network data rate of 10Mbps is supported over broadband Community Antenna Television (CATV) cable, at distances up to 25 miles. Carrier band subnetworks are also cupported, at data rates of 5Mbps, covering a maximum distance of approximately 700 metres. The maximum distances covered by the broadband and carrier band systems are dependent, firstly, upon the characteristics of the cable and, secondly, upon the number of devices on the network (this applies to any network and is not a characteristic of Token/Net).

Token/Net operates over broadband CATV cable concurrently with voice, video, and other CATV services. The network has a fully distributed token bus topology; the bus interface is the Token/Net Interface Module (TIM). The TIM connects data terminals, computers, and other devices to a common cable. The TIM is a special packet assembler/disassembler that assembles port data into packets and transmits the packets over the broadband cable in a time division multiplex fashion. Each TIM consists of a radio frequency modem, media access unit, control unit and power supply. The RF modem operates at 10 Mbps on a midsplit or dual-cable system; it is frequency agile to operate over three channel pairs. Frequency agility allows the connection of different types of equipment to the MAP network using any of the three MAP channels, without the requirement for a different type of interface unit for each piece of equipment. This reduces the level of spares required over a frequency static system.

The MAP channels are IEEE 802.4 designated channels. Each MAP channel is equivalent to two designated channels, with the following frequency allocations:

— Reverse channels

  channel 1: 3'/4' = 59.75-71.75 MHz

  channel 2: 4A'/5' = 71.75-85.75 MHz

  channel 3: 6'/FM1' = 83.75-95.75 MHz

— Forward channels

  channel 1: P/Q = 252-264 MHz

channel 2: R/S = 264-276 MHz

channel 3: T/U = 275-288 MHz

The media access unit implements the IEEE 802.4 token passing access method; the control unit provides TIM management functions and the user interface ports, buffers data for the data port interfaces, and keeps statistics of traffic, data errors and retries. Two TIMs are now available – the Terminal Server TIM and the MAPserver/Plus TIM.

A family of broadband and carrierband component products called MAPware was introduced in January 1986. MAPware consists of board-level interfaces and software through layer 7 of the OSI model, and interchangeable 20Mbps broadband and 5Mbps carrierband modems.

In May 1986 a family of MAP bridges was launched. These were designed to link carrierband to broadband, as well as to provide channel and cross country capabilities. Each member of the family (4100 series) consists of two bridge components interconnected by an asynchronous, full duplex bridge port interface.

A fully configured Token/Net network requires a frequency converter or headend remodulator. Racal-Milgo's headend remodulator is IEEE 802.4 compatible. It is frequency agile over the same range of frequencies as the TIM's RF modem. Figure 4.1 shows the topology of a broadband system, illustrating the transmission of signals to devices via the headend.

Racal-Milgo's Token/Net system software provides the network manager with control over the levels of network services available to each user, along with network management functions. Management tools for the Token/Net local area network are part of the Token/Net management system. This consists of the Token/Net network control computer and the Token/Scope network analyzer. The network control computer is an IBM PC AT-based network management system that allows network managers to configure and control the operational and performance parameters of each TIM.

The Token/Net architecture is layered, to allow the interconnection of multivendor equipment and proprietary communications systems via gateways.

The Token/Net series consists of the following hardware; Terminal Server TIM; Headend Remodulator and Redundancy Switch; MAPserver/Plus TIM; Token/Scope Network; Network Control Computer; MAPware; and MAP Bridges.

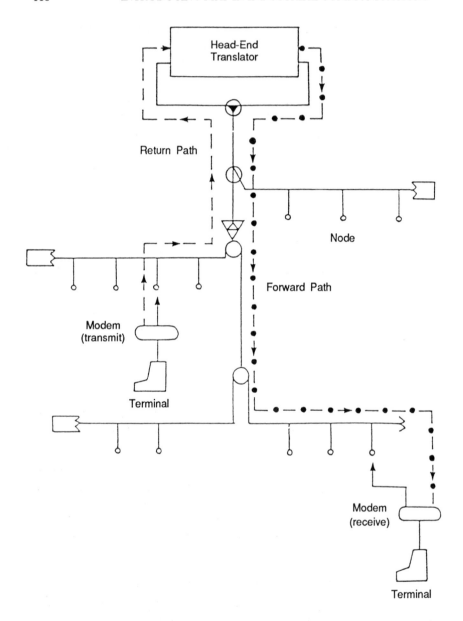

**Figure 4.1    Broadband Topology**

The terminal servers provide connection for devices to the broadband or carrierband network, allowing users to establish point-to-point, multipoint, and broadcast connections. Connections to RS449/422, RS232, IBM, PC, and Multibus are provided by the interface boards.

In September 1987, Concord Communications introduced a bridge to link IEEE 802.3 networks over an IEEE 802.4 broadband backbone. The bridge provides backbone bridging and 802.3 traffic segmentation, combining the best attributes of 802.3 modems and bridges into a single, cost effective solution. In prior application, effective 802.3 bridging solutions required an 802.3 to 802.4 modem as well as an 802.3 bridge.

The Token/Net implementation is an intermediate setup to a MAP compatible network, in the sense that it is merely compatible with MAP version 2.1. The use of Token/Net interface modules allows devices which are non-compatible to be connected to the network. The eventual aim of a MAP network is to remove the requirement for interface units as each device will be OSI and MAP compatible.

Racal have announced a commitment to MAP version 3.0 products. Production of interface units was completed for the Department of Trade and Industry stand at the Enterprise Network Event.

In terms of commercial production, the first products based on version 3.0 (which are likely to be PC interface boards) were available in the third quarter of 1988. Racal's Token Interface Modules, which provide RS232 interconnection, will not be affected by the development of version 3.0. Other Racal bus products, for example connections to Digital Equipment's Q-Bus and Motorola's VME bus, will be fully supported.

The consistency between the physical layers of versions 2.2 and 3.0 means Racal's hardware implementation of these layers is not affected and it will, therefore, be unnecessary to change this hardware in migrating to version 3.0. Layers 3 to 7 have previously been implemented in software. For persons migrating to version 3.0, who previously used Racal software, a free software update will be available.

## 4.3   INDUSTRIAL NETWORKING INCORPORATED

The Company was set up in a joint venture by General Electric and Ungermann-Bass Industrial Network Incorporated (now a wholly owned subsidiary of Ungermann-Bass), and offers a MAP compatible network called MAP/One.

The MAP/One family of products offers a series of board-level MAP interfaces for a variety of systems. Each interface consists of two boards: a controller and a companion broadband or carrierband modem.

All MAP/One board-level interfaces conform with the MAP 2.1/2.2 specification based on the seven layer protocol stack of the ISO OSI model. The MAP protocol uses the IEEE 802.4 token bus local area network standard. The interfaces will support both broadband at 10Mbps and carrierband at 5Mbps. Each pair of interface boards implements the Physical and Data Link layers in hardware and firmware. The remaining five layers of the MAP protocol stack are implemented in the MAP/One software. The software is downloaded directly to the controller card's RAM from the network management console.

The board level interfaces support connections to Multibus, IBM PC, DEC Q-Bus, VMEbus, RS-232, and RS-422.

Two stand-alone MAP/One interface units are available, allowing connection of various types of equipment to an IEEE 802.4 token bus network over serial channels. The MIU-20 is intended for use with terminals, programmable logic controllers and numerical controllers, printers and other devices that communicate over an RS-232 serial interface. The MIU-40 is intended for use with programmable devices such as computers, and machine tool or machine controllers that communicate over an RS-422 serial interface using the HDLC protocol.

The MIU-20 MAP/One interface unit enables up to eight vendor-independent, asynchronous RS-232 serial devices to be connected at speeds up to 19.2 Kbps to a MAP/One network. The interface unit provides the Physical and Data Link layers of the seven-layer model. The operating software provides virtual terminal connections between devices on the network.

The MIU-40 uses a synchronous channel to link devices at a speed up to 56 Kbps to the MAP/One network. Layers 1-2 are provided by hardware and layers 3-7 are provided by software.

MAP/One also has a high-speed MAP bridge and a head-end remodulator. These two components, plus cable, network software and interfaces, comprise a complete MAP/One network.

The high-speed bridge provides transparent connection between broadband and carrierband MAP.

The headend remodulator is frequency agile by manual selection of the required channel. The MAP bridge, Board-level Network Interfaces and Network Interface Units are selected by the user for the channel required. The MAP components can be factory set to the required channel, effectively making them frequency agile (since they can be altered to a different channel if required). MAP/One Application Service Software provides two application interfaces to the user: the MAP application interface which defines a programmatic user interface to the CASE funtions defined in the MAP 2.1/2.2 specification, and the manufacturing message interface which implements a comprehensive library of MMS/MMFS functions. The manufacturing message interface combines high-level MMS services at the user interface level with the required MMFS syntax for the actual messages going over the cable.

The token passing method of media access control is used by MAP/One in exactly the same manner as Racal-Milgo's Token/Net.

The Ungermann-Bass solution to MAP networking is very similar to that of Racal-Milgo; the network is meant as an intermediate step towards total MAP networking, using interfaces to allow compatibility between different devices. Both the Industrial Networking Incorporated and Racal-Milgo solutions are complete solutions for version 2.1/2.2 of MAP.

Ungermann-Bass have announced a commitment to the use of MAP version 3.0 products. Research into the use of version 3.0 has led to the use of Ungermann-Bass products, based on a kernel of version 3.0, in support of the Enterprise Network Event. However, Ungermann-Bass do not believe the MAP version 3.0 specification is sufficiently well defined to justify the sale of products based on the specification. Products will, therefore, be marketed when conformance testing becomes available for MAP version 3.0 products.

For future products, Ungermann-Bass will supply each device with layer 3 to 7 software, enabling it to boot independently of any other device. This will remove the requirement for the network monitor, previously used to download software to each device.

For existing Ungermann-Bass equipment, migration to version 3.0 will be through hardware and/or software, depending upon the circumstances. The software for such an update may be supplied free of charge.

## 4.4 INTEL

Intel's OpenNET is a family of network products that allows applications to transparently access files resident on another computer system across a local area network. The products are based on the OSI seven-layer model.

Intel's MAP solution provides all seven layers of the industry standard ISO/

OSI Manufacturing Automation Protocol for IEEE 802.4 broadband and IEEE 802.3 baseband. The MAP solution comprises three modules: MAP-NET 2.1 networking software, iNA 960 transport and network software, and a MAP board. Together, these three modules provide all seven layers of the ISO/OSI model of the Manufacturing Automation Protocol, version 2.1. MAP-NET 2.1 software provides layers 5 through 7; iNA 960 provides layers 3 and 4, and the MAP board provides layers 1 and 2 in hardware.

OpenNET MAP-NET Communications Software, along with iNA 960 Transport and Network layer software is available in configurable and pre-configured versions to provide an OSI layers 3-7 implementation of the MAP specification. This software executing on an Intel iSBC 554 board provides the data link and the IEEE 802.4 based physical layer for Multibus based systems.

Intel's iNA 960 and its derivative iNA 961 implement the ISO standard for the Class 4 Transport protocols, ISO 8073, and Class 3 Network protocols, ISO 8473. The iNA 960/961 software can support, amongst others, both 802.4 broadband and 802.3 baseband. Since iNA 960 includes a wide variety of data link drivers and a flexible interworking capability, a wide variety of interworking configurations are supportable. An IEEE 802.4 MAP token bus to IEEE 802.3 CSMA/CD router is supported. iNA 961 includes a preconfigured load file for this hardware configuration.

The MAP-NET 2.1 software provides the following MAP application layer functions:

— CASE;

— application subsystem interface;

— FTAM;

— directory services;

— network management.

The software required for layers 3-7 is available as a preconfigured solution, supporting all seven layers on the iSBC 554 Multibus based board. The preconfigured software is loaded to the iSBC 554 board. The user utilities can then communicate with the seven layer protocol stack via the Multibus Interface Protocol.

Intel offers three methods of getting started with MAP; complete broadband MAP, MAP on IEEE 802.3, and MAP broadband/IEEE 802.3 compatibility. The broadband starter kit allows a MAP connection to be set up and expanded.

MAP over IEEE 802.3 is intended for those users wanting to develop MAP compatible software for use on existing IEEE 802.3 networks. The software allows migration to broadband in a simple step, since the software is configurable for both 802.3 and 802.4 based controllers, having the same programming interface. For existing 802.3 networks a router is provided to connect the existing network to MAP.

The iSBC 554 board is frequency static, the channel required being chosen in product ordering. The 554 board and iNA 960/961 software, a broadband cable network and a headend remodulator are the components required to form a complete MAP network. Figure 4.2 shows Intel's MAP-NET user interface.

Intel Corporation, like the previous MAP network manufacturers discussed, have shown a commitment to MAP version 2.1. Intel will wait until a stable specification is available before entering into the market with products based on version 3.0.

For the future, Intel foresee a stable standard, and products based on the standard, by the end of 1988. With the introduction of these, the migration will be via updated software (given free for devices under contract) and a new generation of hardware.

## 4.5   ALLEN-BRADLEY

VistaMAP is a local area network designed to open communication standards supported by many equipment suppliers. VistaMAP supports CATV type broadband at a data rate of 10Mbps and carrierband networks at a data rate of 5 Mbps. As is the case with the MAP networks from Racal-Milgo, Ungermann-Bass and Intel, Allen Bradley's VistaMAP is based on the OSI seven layer model.

The VistaMAP broadband and carrierband products support the IEEE 802.4 token passing standard. The broadband covers a maximum distance of 15 miles (7.5 mile radius), whereas the carrierband is, as with all carrierband networks, more restricted in its length. The communications philosophy is that the user will employ broadband or carrierband networks according to his network application and response time needs.

In many cases the two technologies will be used together, with connection between them provided by a bridge.

Network products can be separated into two categories: interface products and support products.

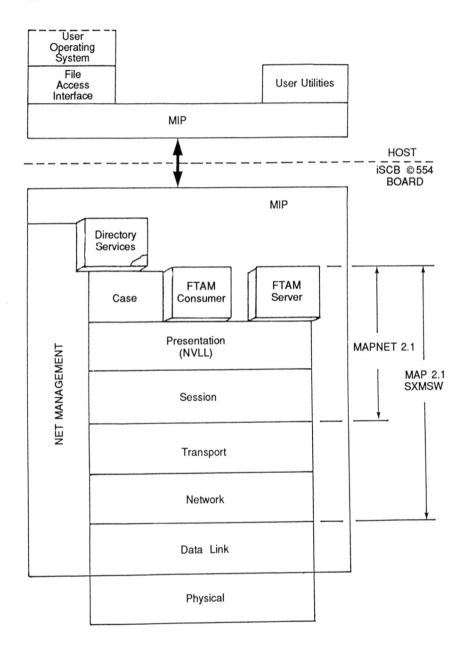

**Figure 4.2    Intel MAP-NET User Interface**

The VistaMAP interface products are the Network Interface Unit and the Network Interface Module. The Network Interface Unit is the basic building block from which several other network interface configurations are built. The Network Interface Unit can be configured to connect synchronous and/or asynchronous devices to the network. RS-232 modules handling data up to 19.2 Kbps provide asynchronous communication. The synchronous interfaces are provided by an HDLC module supporting data rates up to 460.8 Kbps using an RS-449 connection.

Each Network Interface Unit can be configured to support either broadband or baseband. Baseband support is built into the Network Interface Module. Broadband support is provided by an optional module set; the module is frequency agile over the MAP recommended channels.

The network interface modules can accumulate statistics about the traffic it handles, including:

— the number of packets transmitted and received;

— the number of input and output errors;

— the number of retries;

— where transient faults occurred;

— the overall network interface unit status.

The VistaMAP support products are the Network Management Unit, the Network Bridge Unit and the Network Remodulator Unit. As with the MAP networks already discussed, VistaMAP requires a headend remodulator to allow the conversion of transmit signals onto the receive channel, and vice versa. The headend is IEEE 802.4 conformant and is frequency agile, to work over any one of the three recommended MAP channels at a data rate of 10 Mbps. Network management is available through a network management unit. This unit is connected to either a broadband or baseband network via a half bridge.

Bridging can be performed between any combination of the following three media:

— 802.4 broadband

— 802.4 carrierband

— 802.3 baseband

This makes the MAP network a flexible solution allowing connection to many other networks.

Data Highway II is a broadband local area network designed for the plant environment. This network has a transmission rate of 10 Mbps, making it well suited for time-critical operations where the status or position of one device may affect other devices.

Devices which can be connected to Data Highway II include: computers, graphics terminals, programmable controllers, numerical controls, robots and non intelligent devices such as terminals and printers.

Data Highway II uses the token passing method of media access control on a logical ring. The trunkline of Data Highway II is coaxial cable, and can be up to 8000 feet long. Coaxial drop cables join the devices to the trunkline via a local tap. Interface devices are used to connect equipment to the network.

MAP equipment is being produced and used by an increasingly large number of companies. The following section illustrates the use of MAP equipment and networks by some of those companies and the links, where applicable, to proprietary architectures.

## 4.6 DIGITAL EQUIPMENT CORPORATION

DEC's proprietary network architecture, Digital Network Architecture (DNA), is an established network architecture; the first products based on DNA were sold in 1975. In June 1986 DEC announced a programme to implement OSI. Part of the programme was to integrate OSI into DNA. DNA is now based on the International Standards Organisation Open Systems Interconnection (ISO/OSI) seven-layer reference model, and forms the framework for all Digital communication products.

Both DNA and OSI are layered architectures with each layer providing a service to the layer above it whilst using the service provided by the layer below it. Additionally, both are peer-to-peer architectures. DNA has been developed in phases, the current phase being phase IV. The functions and protocols offered by each phase of DNA are implemented by an equivalent phase of the layered software product DECnet. Specific DECnet versions are offered for each of Digital's operating systems.

DNA has eight layers, layer 1-6 broadly corresponding to layers 1-6 in the OSI seven-layer model, and layers 7 and 8 broadly corresponding to layer 7 of the OSI seven-layer model.

Digital's VAX DEC/MAP provides networking services for the manufacturing environment. VAX DEC/MAP is a multivendor, broadband, local area network, which adheres to the Manufacturing Automation Protocol specification 2.1.

VAX DEC/MAP V1.0 consists of both hardware and software. The software implements the network, session and application layers (the presentation layer is null as defined in the MAP 2.1 specification), layers 3 through 7. The physical and data link layers, layers 1 and 2, are IEEE compatible (802.2 Logical Link Control Class 1, 802.4 Token Bus Media Access Control and 802.4 Broadband). They are implemented in hardware using Concord Communications Incorporated (CCI) networking boards. The network media is 75 ohm broadband CATV cable.

The VAX DEC/MAP software provides the user interface to the communication services that consist of File Transfer Access and Management (FTAM), Common Application Service Elements (CASE), Manufacturing Message Format Standard (MMFS), and a software interface at Transport layer 4. The software is a layered product, supported on the VMS operating system. The minimum hardware required consists of:

— any valid VAX and UNIBUS compatible configuration;

— CCI 10 Mbps headend remodulator;

— CCI MAPServer/Plus (TokenNET interface module);

— broadband cable plant.

VAX DEC/MAP can coexist with DECnet on the same broadband cable and on the same VAX host.

## 4.7   BULL

Bull's Distributed Systems Architecture (DSA) networking solution, allowing its own computer families and devices from other manufacturers to intercommunicate.

The fundamental design concepts of DSA include:

— compatibility with international and national standards, providing for long-term investment protection and flexibility in resource selection.

— application independence from specific computer systems for effective resource utilisation and application co-operation.

— modular hardware and software implementations for cost-efficient network configuration and growth.

— compatibility with existing Bull product lines for improved resource accessibility and utilisation.

— comprehensive network management capabilities for productive and responsive network monitoring, control and administration.

— compatibility and coexistence with many non-DSA network protocols and components for improved solution integration.

Based on the ISO/OSI seven-layer reference model, DSA specifies a communications structure divided into seven layers. It specifies how the layers behave individually and how they work together by defining the functions performed by each layer and the protocols that control the dialogue within each layer.

DSA-based networks allow information to be exchanged between two compatible devices without the end user or application being concerned with the details of communication within the network.

### 4.8  MOTOROLA

Motorola is one of the manufacturers providing integrated circuits, VMEsystem boards and software MAP products.

Motorola's MicroMAP software implements the full MAP 2.1 specification. MicroMAP is available with or without board level products. To accommodate various hardware requirements, MicroMAP is offered individually or in combinations, and can be downloaded into RAM or placed in ROM for higher performance and lower cost.

MicroMAP provides users with the Data Link, Network, Transport and Session layers. In addition, MicroMAP features Common Application Service Elements; Manufacturing Message Format Standard; File Transfer, Access and Management; and Directory Services in the Application Layer.

The Token Bus Controller, Carrierband Modem and Broadband Interface Controller chip-level entries form the basis for high performance implementations in the media access control layer, the carrierband physical layer and the digital portion of the broadband physical layer. All three of these components conform to the IEEE 802.4 standard.

The MC68824 Token Bus Controller is a VLSI device which implements the IEEE 802.4 media access control sublayer of the ISO data link layer, supporting a data rate of 1, 5 or 10 Mbps.

The MC68184 broadband interface controller is a 10 Mbps Macrocell Array that manipulates both data and control for the radio frequency transmitter/ receiver circuitry. This device implements the standard MAC/physical serial interface and is designed to connect to the token bus controller.

To implement the IEEE 802.4 Phase Coherent Physical Layer, the MC68194 Carrierband Modem has been developed. The carrierband modem is a large scale integration (LSI) device that interfaces with the token bus controller to provide a node for single channel carrierband networks.

With VMEbus widely used for factory applications, Motorola has acted to provide modular solutions for MAP implementations. All Motorola MAP boards are VME compatible. A MAP VME-compatible board set that incorpo-rates both a MAP interface controller and a broadband modem, is available. Complete software is included to implement layers 1 through 4 of the MAP 2.1 specification. For the most advanced MAP 2.1 compatible token bus node performance, the 10 Mbps MVME372 VMEbus-compatible Advanced MAP Interface Controller is available. This board combines the functionality and performance of the MC68824 token bus controller and the MC68020 micro-processor. The token bus controller implements portions of the MAP 2.1 physical layer and the full media access control functions of the data link layer, while the MC68020 handles the remaining logical link control functions of the data link layer and the remaining layers (3 through 7). Figure 4.3 shows a typical application interface based on Motorola's MAP products.

## 4.9 SIEMENS

Siemens is one of only a few companies worldwide which offers a full range of automation equipment. With the SINEC open systems interconnection, direct communication among all areas of a factory is possible.

SINEC is designed both for processing large quantities of data and for real-time controller-to-controller transmission. Siemens offers both high-speed (SINEC H1) and low cost (SINEC L1) networks for communication between the programmable controllers of SIMATIC S5 systems and other systems, to fit the user's particular needs.

SINEC H1 uses a segmented bus architecture based on Ethernet which has been optimised for use in SIMATIC S5 programmable controllers. H1 will be able to work with MAP compatible devices and systems, regardless of supplier, with the use of a MAP to Ethernet bridge.

The SINEC H1 network has a segmented structure. The transmission

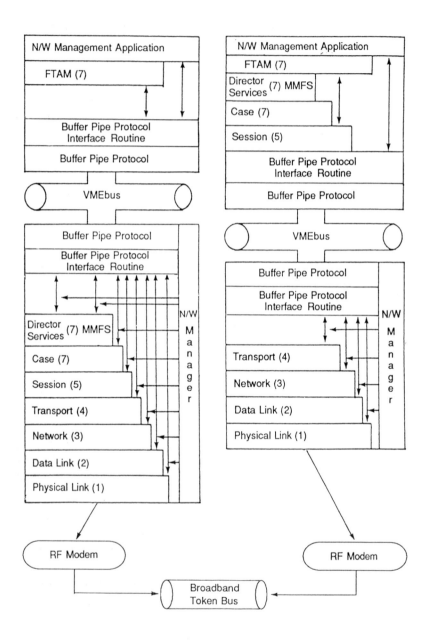

**Figure 4.3    Motorola Application Interface**

medium used is coaxial cable with additional shielding. The network can have a maximum of 1024 users. Each segment can be up to 500 metres in length and can have up to 100 nodes, operating at a rate of 10 Mbps.

The layered structure of SINEC H1 and its use of the OSI protocols allow it to be connected to MAP networks via the use of interfaces. SINEC H1 was designed with open systems in mind but is clearly designed to be used as a proprietary network linking programmable controllers, numerical controllers and robots, which can then be linked to MAP via a gateway. This allows an existing proprietary network to operate at the present time with connection to a factory wide network, running MAP, at a later date. Figure 4.4 shows the structure MAP, in relation to Siemens proprietary networks, within a corporate communications structure.

SINEC L1 is designed for applications with lower speed requirements. SINEC L1 is a bus system with serial data transmission on the master slave principle. Up to 30 programmable controllers can be controlled by one master. The individual nodes can be up to 63 km apart. The transmission rate is 9600 bps.

In SINEC L1, the master gives each slave the right to access the bus in turn. The slave can then pass data directly to another programmable controller. This method means the information flow is not routed via the master and the master is therefore free to perform others tasks. SINEC L1 also has priority job processing facilities.

## 4.10   TEXAS INSTRUMENTS

Texas Instruments have designed a software and hardware product range to provide connectivity between factory floor intelligent machines and Texas Instruments' HDLC-based local area network, TIWAY I. This range of products is generally known as Unilink.

Unilink is based on the ISO/OSI reference model. Unilink allows communication with a wide range of computer numerical control machines, robots, PLCs, intelligent instruments, process equipment and computer peripherals connected to the TIWAY I network. Unilink supports local response to machine communications and multidrop addressing to reduce host computer workload.

TIWAY I was designed for data acquisition and supervisory control. It is an open serial communication network using a twisted pair cable, incorporating shielding for noise immunity, over distances of 7600 metres with up to 254 connections, transmitting up to speeds of 115 Kbps.

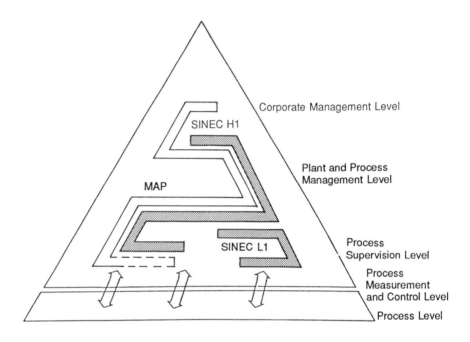

**Figure 4.4    Siemens Proprietory Network Structure**

The Unilink host adaptor provides TIWAY I network management services for a variety of different host computers. It allows a host to communicate with devices on the network via Network Interface Modules.

The TIWAY I secondary adaptor links RS232 compatible intelligent factory floor devices to the TIWAY I local area network, via an RS232 connector.

The final member of the Unilink family is the TIWAY I network interface module. This is used to connect PLCs to the TIWAY I network.

Texas Instruments' TIWAY II is a MAP compatible broadband factory communications backbone. It operates at 10Mbps in the mid split configuration. The TIWAY II gateway provides protocol translation between the TIWAY I local area network and MAP networks (including TIWAY II).

The gateway conforms to the IEEE 802.4 token passing bus protocol. Direct connection to TIWAY I is via a high speed communication card. The interface can allow either a connection to twisted pair, or connection to RS232/RS422 with modems (over an unlimited distance).

The TIWAY II gateway allows any equipment connected to TIWAY I to communicate the broadband MAP network. Figure 4.5 shows a typical application of Texas's proprietary networks TIWAY I and II.

## 4.11   GOULD

Gould's MODBUS II is a set of local area network interface products which conform with the Manufacturing Automation Protocol Enhanced Performance Architecture (MAP/EPA). Existing MODBUS software is compatible with MODBUS II allowing interconnection between the two.

The MODBUS II interface module provides peer-to-peer communications over the standard MAP/EPA network for the 984 family of programmable controllers. The interface is IEEE 802.4 and IEEE 802.2 compatible, transmitting at 5 Mbps over carrierband. The interface module can support up to 60 nodes with a maximum cable length of 4000 feet (depending on the number of nodes attached).

The Gould FM 1800 cell controller allows numerous plant floor communication devices to be controlled during connection to a 10 Mbps MAP version 2.1 network. The cell controller can support up to 1024 direct input/output points.

The Gould NW 0200 MAP gateway provides a means of integrating diverse, segmented manufacturing systems along MAP backbone networks, without replacing existing equipment. The gateway is a non-vendor specific device for operation on a MAP version 2.1 network. Using all seven layers of the ISO/OSI model, the gateway performs protocol translations to connect different network architecture along a MAP controlled network.

## 4.12   IBM

The current position of MAP within IBM (UK) is presently that of the IBM Corporation at the time of AUTOFACT '87. At the AUTOFACT demonstration in Detroit, support for the connection of the IBM System/370 processors to a MAP 2.1 network was announced. The connection to the MAP network will be via Industrial Networking Incorporated cards in IBM LAN Channel Attachments. The demonstration of AUTOFACT presented a distributed implementation of plant floor control running on two IBM system platforms, the IBM 9370 Information System and the IBM 7552 Industrial Computer.

In 1985, IBM announced the Series/1 Real-Time Programming System (RPS) MAP Communications Server (MCS) and the Series/1 Event Driven

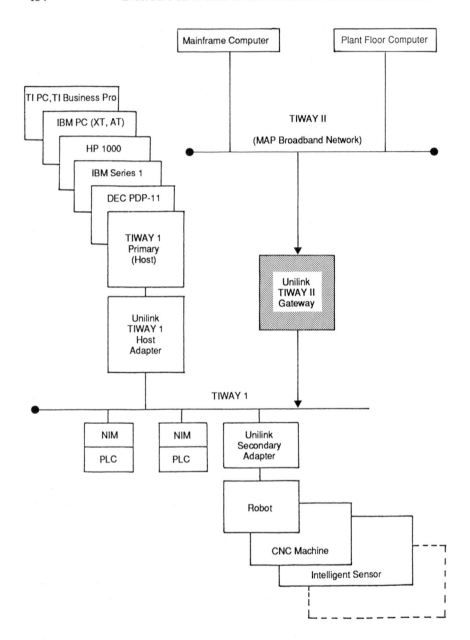

**Figure 4.5    Texas TIWAY I and II**

Executive (EDX) MAP Application Server (MAS), to provide a communications and applications gateway between SNA and certain MAP applications. The MCS supports connections between open systems through a network interface unit attached to an IEEE 802.4 local area network and through the RPS X.25/High-Level Data Link Control (HDLC) Communications Support program.

The communications server supports MAP network user access to files and applications residing on an IBM System/370, 43XX or 30XX host through File Transfer Access Management (FTAM). It also supports Directory services which provide users with network application information. The EDX MAP Application Server also codes and decodes Manufacturing Message Format Standard (MMFS) messages. These MMFS formats are used to address the bidirectional transfer of digitally encoded manufacturing information. In so doing, the MAP application server provides MMFS application and presentation layer protocols, which enable communications between the following:

— programmable controllers;

— numerical controllers;

— robotic controllers;

— specialised systems, including vision systems, probe systems, and welding controllers;

— data terminal equipment, including hosts, minicomputers and workstations.

The following statements of direction was given from IBM:

IBM is committed to MAP version 3.0 as the solution for Plant Operations communications.

IBM intends to provide a means for application migration across IBM MAP 2.1 and MAP 3.0 products.

In addition, IBM plans to extend communications and systems management offerings to include management of MAP 3.0 networks.

In general, IBM policy is to provide products after the standards have been approved, using business judgement as to the priority of implementation and options supported.

IBM's proprietary network architecture, Systems Network Architecture (SNA), exists in parallel with OSI networks. IBM has products that provide for conversion from SNA to services and protocols defined within all seven OSI layers, allowing interconnection of the wide range of devices running SNA with OSI devices.

## 4.13   SUMMARY

Obtaining information on the products available for MAP networks leads to two major conclusions. Firstly, the market for MAP products has not yet grown sufficiently large to warrant a significant level of competition among suppliers; the four major suppliers of MAP networks have a hold on the market with smaller companies being noticeable by their absence. Secondly, due to the updating of the specification to version 3.0, many of the products are still based on version 2.1. The launch of more 3.0 products should follow the Enterprise Network Event.

Although all major computer manufacturers are seen to be involved, they are reserved in their approach to the products available and in some cases are 'sitting on the fence' while the work is being completed. This is I believe, a sound business-like approach when trying to deal with what is after all a specification, albeit a currently stable one.

Europe is a prime user of IEEE 802.3. Because of this, IEEE 802.3 will gain in stature in the MAP specification. At the same time I am sure that a number of suppliers will take a long hard look at their product development and related future business.

# 5 Establishing a Role for MAP

Support for MAP and migration and compatibility issues are critical because, as MAP takes its place in the communications hierarchies of organisations, the support it receives is the difference between success and failure. By the same token it will only receive support to the extent to which it provides what the user wants. This chapter is meant to put MAP into perspective and help organisations come to terms with the positioning of MAP within their own company using the theory of the previous chapters and the practical considerations of products and systems in Chapter 4. MAP was a means to an end for General Motors. However, the functions which MAP provides, and the solution it is putting forward to communications problems, must be kept in perspective with an organisation's overall communications and business requirements.

Organisations going through the process of evaluating MAP for use within their own company should understand that MAP will not satisfy everyone's requirements immediately. The qualification of this statement arises primarily from the fact that not all of the industrial communications networks evolve at the same rate. If a sample is taken from the sufficiently large population of industrial companies then it can be found through an analysis of their communications networks that the results will tend towards a Gaussian (or normal) distribution (see Figure 5.1).

This suggests that there will always be companies on the extreme right of the side of this distribution – the type of company already heavily committed to installing networking and automation equipment in its plants. By the same reasoning there will always be companies on the extreme left-hand side of the distribution – those companies only just beginning to think about networking.

The majority of companies fall somewhere within the middle ground. They may already have some communications in place (not necessarily networks) but almost certainly each constituent part of the communications facility will have

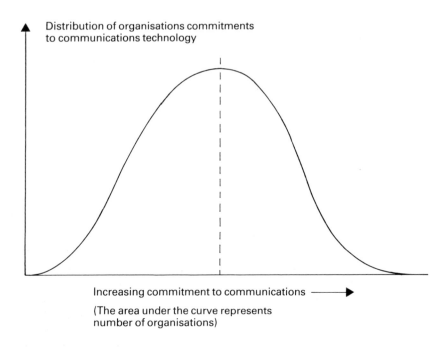

Distribution of organisations commitments
to communications technology

Increasing commitment to communications ⟶

(The area under the curve represents
number of organisations)

**Figure 5.1   Distribution of Companies Committed to Communications**

evolved in its own unique way. This is true not only of manufacturing data but also of voice communication and non-manufacturing data. (Non-manufacturing data cannot logically exist in a manufacturing organisation whose prime function is the production of saleable units. However, for the sake of clarity, I will continue to refer to manufacturing data as, for example, part programs; and non-manufacturing data as, for example, financial information.)

The remainder of this chapter gives pointers on how to evaluate whether MAP is applicable for particular communications requirements.

The consistent analysis of the distribution described above is made more complex when geographical regional variations are taken into account (the needs and expertise of organisations within Europe do not follow exactly the same pattern of similar organisations in the United States – where MAP originated). Thus we may conclude that the evolution of an organisation's network and the definition of its future networking requirements depend ultimately on:

— the positioning of the organisation in relation to the normal distribution described above;

— the future networking needs of the organisation in relation to its corporate plan;

— the ability of technology to satisfy those needs in a cost effective way;

— the availability of the technology within the organisation's geographical area.

Keeping these four points in mind, we can now use General Motors as an example and examine its present and future requirements and where MAP would fit in. Applying the previous normal distribution model to the General Motors environment we find, through an analysis of the four points, that:

— General Motors are a company predominantly on the right-hand side of this distribution curve and as such their capital expenditure on new plant automation equipment was, and is, colossal. They needed to buy equipment from many different vendors in order to satisfy specific plant needs and consequently there was a requirement for the equipment to interwork, not just to interface. This immediately caused problems because of the proprietary communications used by each particular vendor. General Motors were spending increasing amounts of money on 'black boxes' to allow different types of equipment to talk to each other.

— In relation to the corporate plan, General Motors saw itself spending more in the future on automation equipment and consequently, because of its present situation, more on the 'black boxes' which had become essential for effective communications. The need had arisen for a common communications protocol serving all equipment.

— The current technology was able to provide a solution but not in a cost effective way due to the increased spending on 'black boxes'.

— General Motors already had in place a number of communications networks – basic infrastructure – but what was needed was the definition of a protocol stack encompassing the users' requirements. In addition there were international standards available for use but there were also recognised holes.

We have seen that the outcome of this analysis led to the definition of the MAP architecture as described in Chapter 2 and the MAP specification described in Chapter 3. It is only when MAP is then used within the corporate network architecture that problems start to arise, at the present time due to a number of fundamental reasons:

—  MAP is still an evolving specification and as such presents the user community with a somewhat moving target, although General Motors has gone some way towards solving this problem by attempting to freeze the MAP version 3.0 specification for a number of years.

—  Broadband installations are more common in the USA than in Europe, although again there is increased support for MAP protocols over Ethernet.

—  Many organisations (especially in Europe) already have their networks based on Ethernet, baseband systems.

So where does this leave MAP networks which are based purely on broadband? Clearly unless organisations are fortunate enough to have the benefit of a 'green field' site the main requirement is for a migration strategy incorporating broadband or carrierband (organisations in the USA do not have to justify the underlying broadband network first – it is usually already in place!). In order to find the level where MAP will fit into a corporate network the following guidelines are recommended:

—  plan and install broadband (this is a non-trivial task and should not be underestimated). Analysis of requirements may show that carrierband is more appropriate;

—  define the voice and data requirements (MAP specifies PBX connections);

—  define the information flows within the plant;

—  define the eventual communications architecture within the plant;

—  define the wide area network communications requirements.

If these guidelines are followed it will be easier to establish which equipment will be affected by MAP and to take account of this in invitations to tender for future needs.

It must be concluded that there can be no hard and fast rule for the adoption of MAP within any organisation. Given N different companies there are likely to be N different migration plans. This is not meant as a 'get out' but must be accepted as a fact of life. The 'bottom line' questions to be asked in relation to the direction of communications technology are:

What will MAP give me?

Are the products available?

Will it be cost effective to implement?

These are not straightforward questions and must be viewed with the company's long-term strategy in mind. Trying to answer these questions based on an organisation's short-term requirements is foolhardy.

Taken in relation to an organisation's corporate strategy and the suppliers' attitude to MAP – as the use of proprietary networks can still form part of the migration path towards MAP – answering the questions above should point the way to where the MAP can be placed within an organisation's corporate communications hierarchy.

If organisations look at the prospect of using MAP it will force them at least to scrutinise their own, often neglected, corporate communications infrastructure. In consequence they will be better placed to assess their own future requirements with respect to the more fundamental issue – that of integration.

# 6 Advancing the MAP Specification

Undoubtedly 'demonstrator events' have provided the impetus for MAP (and indeed OSI) development. No event has been more instrumental in this than the Enterprise Network Event.

The Enterprise Network Event (ENE) was held on June 6-8, 1988, in Baltimore USA in an opportunity to orchestrate an open systems interconnection solution to corporate communications. The combination of inter-operable multivendor systems with applicability to every sector of industry culminated in such a solution.

Whilst CIMAP, held in Birmingham UK in December 1986, was a valuable tool for showing manufacturing industry the actual progress made up to 1986, ENE illustrated the progress made on product development to the more comprehensive version 3.0 of MAP and TOP, which was officially released to the event.

Nine sponsored cells were integrated at the event – illustrating the reality of MAP/TOP 3.0 specifications. The UK Department of Trade and Industry cell was one of the nine – showing various functional activities found within such an operation. These ranged from the commercial department – receiving electronic mail, preparing quotations, undertaking design work – through production planning and scheduling – to production, assembly, quality control, testing, dispatch and finally back to electronic mail for invoicing and collection of factory statistics.

The nine sponsored cells were:

The UK Department of Trade and Industry

US Process Industries – staged by the Aluminium Company of America

143

John Deere & Company

Boeing Computer Services

TRW

General Motors

Aerospace – US Air Force

Communication Network for Manufacturing Applications (CNMA)

Corporation for Open Systems (COS)

The ENE event was sponsored jointly by the US MAP/TOP Users Group and the Corporation for Open Systems. The MAP/TOP Users Group was formed in 1984 to lobby for the international adoption and development of the MAP/TOP specifications. COS is a US based international consortium of vendors and users of computer and communications products and services. Its long range objective is to provide an international vehicle for accelerating the introduction of interoperable, multi-vendor products and services operating under agreed OSI, ISDN (Integrated Services Digital Network) and related international standards to assure acceptance of an open network architecture in world markets.

The sheer scope of the organisations involved will ensure that commitment is maintained to OSI in general and MAP, and other relevant functional profiles in particular.

# Appendix 1
# Glossary

**ABM**                      Asynchronous Balanced Mode; a mode of operation defined within HDLC which covers point-to-point communication. Polling is not required and either station is allowed to transmit without permission from the other. This is identical to LAPB. There are a number of other modes of operation within HDLC.

**Abstract Transfer Syntax**  Part of the presentation layer but specified by entities in the application layer, it is concerned with the type of information to be transferred. Together with a compatible CTS is referred to as presentation context.

**Acknowledge**              Message sent by receiving station to indicate that a frame has been received without errors.

**ACSE**                     Associated Control Service Elements. Functions defined as part of the application layer, common to a number of application services (DIS 8649/2 and DIS 8650/20).

**ADCCP**                    Advanced Data Communications Control Protocol; a bit-oriented synchronised data link control protocol standard adopted by ANSI. Functionally indentical to HDLC.

**ADD**                      Addendum to OSI full international standard (eg IS08348/ADD1).

**Addressing**               This is a critical issue particularly at the network layer where ISO 8348/ADD2 exists. Work is required at a national level to decide upon an actual numbering scheme in line with ISO goals.

**Alternate Routeing**    A technique used within networks for varying the route of the traffic depending upon loading and availability of channels.

**ANSA**    Advanced Network Systems Architecture; a UK Alvey project to investigate performance effect OSI.

**ANSI**    American National Standards Institute; US standards organisation.

**Application-entity**    The part of an application process which concerns OSI.

**Application Process**    An OSI term to describe a user of the OSI infrastructure – whether it be an application program, a human operator or a process control device.

**Architecture**    A framework for a computer or communications system which defines its functions, interfaces and procedures.

**ASCII**    The American Standard Code for Information Interchange; based on the ISO 7-bit data code, usually transmitted in 8-bit data code incorporating a parity bit.

**ASN.1**    Abstract Syntax Notation One; part of the OSI presentation layer standards (ISO 8824 and ISO 8825).

**Asynchronous**    Simple communication of data character by character, which generally relies on a host for screen formatting.

**AUTOFACT**    US trade show at which MAP and TOP demonstrations have taken place.

**BAS**    Basic Activity Subset; one of the defined subsets of the session layer (ISO 8326 and ISO 8327).

| | |
|---|---|
| BCS | Basic Combined Subset; one of the defined subsets of the session layer. |
| Bit | Binary digit; when referred to in bits per second (or bps) it indicates the transmission rate of a communications link. |
| Blocking | A function which takes multiple SDUs from the layer above and creates a single PDU. |
| Bridge | A device which allows two similar LANs using the same protocol to be interconnected. No modification is made to either the content or format of the data passing through the device. |
| Broadband | A LAN signalling technique that utilises frequency division multiplexing (FDM) to carry many independent channels simultaneously. Generally uses either a one or two cable system as its physical transmission medium. |
| BSI | British Standards Institution; UK standards organisation. |
| BSS | Basic Synchronised Subset; one of the defined subsets of the session layer (ISO 8326 and OSI 8327). |
| CASE | Common Application Service Elements; a set of OSI layer 7 standards which provide common functions for the application programs and other application layer standards (DIS 8649 and DIS 8650). No longer widely used – more likely to see ACSE and CCR. |
| CCITT | The International Consultative Committee on Telephony and Telegraphy (part of the International Telecommunication Union, an agency of the UN); one of the leading international standards-making organisations, comprising mainly PTTs (national postal, telephone and telegraphy organisations). |
| CCR | Commitment, Concurrency and Recovery; |

|   |   |
|---|---|
|   | functions defined as part of CASE which are common to many specific applications (DIS 8649/3 and DIS 8650/3). |
| **CEN** | European Committee for Standardisation. European counterpart of ISO. |
| **CENELEC** | European Committee for Electrotechnical Standardisation. European counterpart of IEC. |
| **CEPT** | European Conference of Posts and Telecommunications. CCITT counterpart for Europe. |
| **CIM** | Computer Integrated Manufacture; manufacture controlled and co-ordinated by computers with only minimal human intervention. |
| **Circuit-switching** | One of the major classes of network, whereby a circuit is established and maintained between the communicating parties for the duration of the 'call' (on the public telephone network) and is then disconnected, in constrast with 'non-switched' communications over point-to-point links. |
| **Class Negotiation** | Used in the transport protocol, a process whereby specific options are selected for a particular connection. |
| **CLNS** | Connectionless-Oriented Network Service. |
| **Concrete Transfer Syntax (CTS)** | Used to represent information transferred between end systems as agreed between those end systems. It is part of the presentation layer. |
| **Connectionless Service** | Where no permanent section can be assumed, and no connection establishment takes place prior to communication. |
| **Connection-oriented** | Where a permanent connection (either logical or physical) exists for the duration of the communication. |
| **CONS** | Connection-Oriented Network Service. |

COS                             Corporation for Open Systems; USA-based
                                organisation sponsored by a number of suppliers
                                and large users, involved in research, standards
                                development and standard promotion.

COTP                            Connection-Oriented Transport Protocol.

CSMA/CD                         Carrier Sense Multiple Access with Collision
                                Detection; one of the major classes of low level
                                access techniques, and a method of preventing
                                data corruption used mainly for local area
                                networks (LANs). Ethernet is an example of this
                                type. It is specified in OSI Standard ISO 8802/3,
                                based upon the work of IEEE committee 802.3
                                (802.3 is not, however the same as Ethernet).

Cyclic Redundancy Check         Scheme for error detection employed by HDLC.
(CRC)

DAD                             Addendum to a standard at DIS status (eg ISO
                                8073/DAD2).

Data Link Control               The second layer of the OSI reference model at
                                which blocks of data are reliably transmitted
                                over an imperfect transmission link.

DCTE                            Data Circuit Termination Equipment; a CCITT
                                term referring to equipment which carried out
                                signal conversion and coding on the line (eg
                                modem or equivalent).

DIS                             Draft International Standard; final stage prior to
                                becoming a full international standard from ISO
                                (eg DIS 7942).

DP                              Draft Proposal; a proposed standard from ISO at
                                the first stage of development but with some
                                technical stability (eg DP 8613).

DTE                             Data Terminal Equipment; a CCITT term
                                referring to the terminal or computer equipment
                                which is the origin or destination of data traffic.
                                A DCE is required for connection to remote
                                DTE.

| | |
|---|---|
| **ECMA** | European Computer Manufacturers Association (a trade organisation very active in international standards making). |
| **EIA** | Electronic Industries Association (a US based standards organisation, principally concerned with low-level electrical interfaces). |
| **EN** | European Norme; a standard within the European Community. |
| **End system** | Strictly used in the OSI context to define an 'open system' that can communicate with other end systems via OSI protocols, as distinct from a Relay or Gateway that performs an intermediate routeing function. |
| **Entity** | Active element within one OSI layer which employs the services of the next lower layer to communicate with a peer entity. |
| **ENV** | European pre-standards from CEN/CENELEC/CEPT. |
| **ESPRIT** | European Strategic Program of Research in Information Technology. |
| **Ethernet** | A type of local area network based upon CSMA/CD technology – originally developed by DEC, Intel and Xerox. |
| **EurOSInet** | European demonstration of an OSI network by a number of leading vendors. |
| **Frame** | A unit of HDLC. A sequence of bits which make up a valid message, containing flags, control field, address field, a frame check sequence, and optionally an information field. |
| **FTAM** | File Transfer, Access and Management – of the protocols being developed for the OSI application layer; specified in DIS 8571. |
| **Functional Standards** | Indentified 'stacks' of base standards to allow the construction of interworking products. |

| | |
|---|---|
| **Gateway** | An intermediate system in the communication between two or more end systems which are not directly linked and/or observe different protocols (eg between an OSI system and a non-OSI system). |
| **GKS** | Graphics Kernel System; standards for computer graphics, current reference is ISO 7942. |
| **GOSIP** | Government OSI Profile – in the UK and USA. |
| **HDLC** | High-level Data Link Control; a standard for frame structures in connection with data communications protocols, at the data link layer (ISO 3309 is concerned with HDLC frame structure). |
| **Host** | A computer system on which applications can be executed and which also provides a service to connected users and devices. |
| **IEC** | International Electrotechnical Commission. |
| **IEEE** | Institute of Electrical and Electronic Engineers (of America); another organisation active in standards making, mainly relevant for LANs. |
| **Interconnection** | A term often used to define a lesser level than full interworking, such that two computer systems can communicate and exchange data but without consideration of how the dialogue between applications processes is controlled or how the data is presented and recognised. |
| **Interworking** | Ultimately, the achievement of proper and effective communication of 'linking' between different applications processes or programs and data; may be on different systems from different manufacturers, remote from each other and connected by some transmission medium or network. |
| **IS** | International Standards; fully agreed and published ISO standard (eg ISO 7498). |

**ISDN**            Integrated Services Digital Network; this will be OSI-compatible at the lower layers.

**ISO**             International Standards Organisation; major body responsible for the development of OSI standards.

**IT**              Information Technology; a term used to encompass the methods and techniques used in information handling and retrieval by automatic means, including computing, telecommunications and office systems.

**JTM**             Job Transfer and Manipulation; one of the protocols being developed for the OSI application layer for activating and controlling remote processing (DP 8831 and 8832).

**Kernel**          Service elements within the session layer which are necessary to set up and close down a connection; part of ISO 8326 and ISO 8327. Also used to describe basic elements of CASE (DIS 8649 and DIS 8650).

**LAN**             Local Area Network; spans a limited geographical area (usually a building or a site) and interconnects a variety of computers and other devices, usually at very high data rates.

**LAPB**            Link Access Procedure Balanced; a variant of HDLC used between peer systems which is the basis for layer 2 of X.25 (as an example of standards in this area, ISO 7776 is concerned with X.25 compatible DTE Data Link Procedure).

**Layer**           In the ISO Reference Mode, used to define a discrete level of function within a communications context with a defined service interface – alternative protocols for a particular layer should then be interchangeable without impact on adjoining layers.

**LLC1 AND LLC2**   Logical Link Control One and Two; level 2 protocols defined for LANs. Provide support for medium independent data link functions. Uses the MAC sublayer to provide services to the network layer. LLC1 is for a connectionless link, and LLC2 is for connection-oriented (ISO 8802/2).

**Logical Channel**

In X.25 single physical channel between DTE and DCE can be multiplexed to allow a number of virtual calls to take place concurrently.

**MAC**

Medium Access Control; a sublayer comprising part of the data link and/or physical layers that supports topology-dependent functions (ie dependent upon the type of LAN) and uses the services of the physical layer to provide services to the logical link control sublayer.

**MAP**

Manufacturing Automation Protocol; originally initiated by General Motors in order to force suppliers to adhere to a prescribed set of standards.

**Medium**

The physical component of a network that interlinks devices and provides the pathway over which data can be conveyed. Examples include coaxial cable and optical cable.

**MHS**

Message Handling Service; a general term for the application layer standards being defined by X.400.

**MOTIS**

Message Oriented Text Interchange Systems; a set of text handling standards under development by ISO, with a greater scope than X.400. (DP 8505.2, DP 8883, DP 9065, DP 9066.)

**MTA**

Message Transfer Agent; system responsible for storage and delivery of messages in MHS.

**Multiplexing**

The carrying of more than one data stream over the same connection (apparently) simultaneously.

| | |
|---|---|
| **NBS** | The USA National Bureau of Standards; organises workshops on OSI and OSINET. |
| **Network** | A collection of equipment and/or transmission facilities for communication between computer systems (whether a single dedicated link, line, dial-up PSTN (telephone) line, public or private data network (PDN), satellite link, etc) more correctly in the OSI context used to define the achievement of end-to-end communication between end systems, however accomplished. |
| **Network Architectures** | A generic term for the layered approach which individual vendors take towards development of their communications and applications products. Examples include IBM and SNA, DEC, and DNA, Bull and DSA, and ICL and IPA and work connected with vendor independent stan dardisation, largely carried out under the guid- ance of ISO. |
| **OSI Gateway** | A method of providing access to an OSI network from a non-OSI system by mapping the sets of protocols together. |
| **OSI Reference Model** | Seven layer model defined by an ISO subcommittee as a framework around which an Open Systems Architecture can be built. It describes the conceptual structure of systems which are to communicate. |
| **OSINET** | An OSI demonstration network organised by NBS in the United States. |
| **OTSS** | Open Systems Transport and Session Support; IBM mainframe software providing OSI transport and session services. |
| **P1, P2, P3, P7** | Different classes of Protocol specified within the CCITT X.400 (MHS) standards. |
| **Packet Switching** | A type of data network based upon the CCITT X.25 recommendation, whereby a 'virtual call' is established, but individual data 'packets' may |

| | |
|---|---|
| | be routed across separate physical links through the network. |
| **PAD** | Packet Assembler/Disassembler; converts data at a terminal into 'packets' (discrete quantities) for transmission over a communications line and sets addresses calls to another PAD (or system with equivalent functionality). It permits terminals which cannot otherwise connect directly to a packet switched network to access such networks. |
| **PCI** | Protocol Control Information; control information passed between peer entities to coordinate the transfer of user data. It is added to the Service Data Unit to create a Protocol Data Unit. |
| **PDU** | Protocol Data Unit; created at a given layer in the stack by taking the service data unit from the layer above and adding PCI. This is the information which is passed to the peer entity. |
| **Peer Entity** | Active element within an OSI layer which corresponds to an equivalent element in the corresponding layer of a different end system. |
| **Physical Layer** | This is the first level of the OSI Reference Model, responsible for transmitting bit streams between data link entities across physical connections. |
| **Presentation Layer** | Level 6 in the model; for agreement on how information is presented. |
| **Protocol** | A set of rules for the interaction of two or more parties engaged in data transmission or communication. In OSI terms interaction between two layers of the same status in different systems. |
| **Protocol Stack** | The set of OSI protocols at all seven layers required for a particular function or implemented in a particular system. |

**PSDN**               Public Switched Data Network; CCITT term for public packet switched network.

**PSE**                 Packet Switched Exchange; a switching computer which adheres to X.25 packet-level procedures.

**PSTN**               Public Switching Telephone Network.

**PTT**                 National postal, telephone and telegraphy organisation.

**Relay**               A term used for a system which performs an intermediate function in the communication between two or more end systems (eg a node in a public switched network).

**Routeing**           Function within a layer to translate title or address of an entity into a path through which the entity can be reached.

**ROSE**             Research Open Systems for Europe.

**SAP**                Service Access Point; allows entities with adjacent layers to interact (see NSAP).

**SASE**              Specific Application Service Elements; those parts of the OSI Application Layer which include FTAM, JTM, VT and MOTIS.

**SC**                  Subcommittee; within ISO, SC21 has responsibility for development of standards for OSI layers 5 to 7, SC6 for layers 1 to 4, SC18 for message handling systems.

**SDF**                Simple Document Formattable; the most basic structure for text interchange.

**SDU**               Service Data Unit; the unit which is passed from the layer above, when combined with the PCI it forms that layer's PDU.

**Segmenting**      A function to map one SDU into multiple SDUs.

**Service**          The interface between a layer and the next higher layer (in the same system), ie the features of that

|  | layer (and below) which are available for selection and the conditions reported. |
|---|---|
| **Service Primitive** | The elements defined in one type of ISO OSI standard which specify in a precise manner the services provided by a particular layer. |
| **Session** | A period during which a connection exists between two points in a network such that data and/or commands may be exchanged. |
| **Session Layer** | Fifth layer in the model, responsible for managing and coordinating the dialogue between end systems. |
| **Slotted Ring** | One of the types of local area network, specified in DP 8802/6 and by a British Standard; a Cambridge Ring is an example. |
| **SNA** | IBM's proprietary Systems Network Architecture, which is layered but at present has only some architectural similarity to OSI. |
| **SNACP** | SubNetwork Access Protocol; the lowest sublayer of the network layer, X.25 is an example of an SNACP. It provides a service to the next sublayer. |
| **SNDCP** | SubNetwork Dependent Convergence Protocol; this sublayer maps a consistent standardised service onto the service provided by the subnetwork. |
| **SNICP** | SubNetwork Independent Convergence Protocol; this sublayer provided the network service to the transport layer (only two SNICPs are required – one for connectionless and one for connection-oriented service). |
| **SPAG** | Standards Promotion and Application Group – a consortium of European suppliers developing functional standards. |
| **Sublayer** | A group of functions in a layer. A sublayer can be null if there is no function to perform. |

**Subnetwork**

The more correct term in the OSI context for a physical network which may in fact be only one in a series of such physical networks which links two or more end systems.

**TC**

Technical Committee; within ISO, TC97 has responsibility for SC6, SC18 and SC21, which are the primary sub-committees developing OSI standards.

**Teletex**

An international service for document interchange, which provides rapid exchange of text via the telephone network and other public data networks. Unlike telex, teletex is a method rather than a specific network or system (CCITT F.200, T.60, T.61 and T.62).

**Token Bus**

One of the types of local area network, specified in ISO 8802/4 and IEEE 802.4.

**Token Passing**

A class of local area network using a 'token'– data and protocol information in a standard format – as the means of moving messages between devices. Only the device holding a 'token' may pass messages.

**Token Ring**

One of the types of local network, specified in ISO 8802/5 and IEEE 802.5; the type of LAN given primary support by IBM. This type of LAN employs a system of token passing.

**TOP**

Technical and Office Protocols; a set of functional standards designed for the office environment, initiated by Boeing in the US.

**Transport Classes**

The method by which the options of the transport layer are grouped into five subsets.

**Transport Layer**

Fourth level of the Reference Model, charged with guaranteeing end-to-end communication between end systems.

**Triple X**

The CCITT recommendations X.3, X.28 and X.29 – which jointly define standards for

| | |
|---|---|
| | asynchronous terminals to access a mainframe (or X.25 packet terminal) via a PAD. |
| UA | User Agent; within MHS, the system responsible for originating and receiving messages. |
| Virtual Circuit | A logical transmission path through an X.25 packet switched network established by the exchange of set-up messages between two DTEs. The circuit may use more than one physical circuit, or share a physical circuit with other virtual circuits. |
| VTP | Virtual Terminal Protocol, one of the protocols being developed for the OSI application layer for standard terminal access to computer systems (DP9040 and DP9041). |
| WAN | A Wide Area Network; makes use of communications facilities which can carry data to remote sites; could be a public data network (PDN) such as BT's PSS or a private network. |
| X.3, X.28, X.29 | The set of Triple-X protocols. |
| X.21 | The CCITT Recommendation defining interfaces for synchronous transmission over Public Data Networks (circuit-switched networks). |
| X.25 | The CCITT Recommendation defining interfaces to packet-mode terminals on packet-switched networks, as used by British Telecom's PSS and many other national and private networks. |
| X.25 (1980), X.25 (1984) | The variants of X.25 agreed by CCITT at its plenary meetings in 1980 and 1984, respectively. The 1980 version is a subset of the 1984 version. |
| X.400 | The CCITT series of Message Handling Service Recommendations for text interchange which |

will precede, but be similar to, the final ISO standards (MOTIS) for message handling and document interchange.

**X-OPEN**    A European venture between manufacturers outside the bounds of the OSI model, to create software portability between a variety of computer systems.

# Appendix 2

# MAP and TOP Specification Summary for Version 3.0

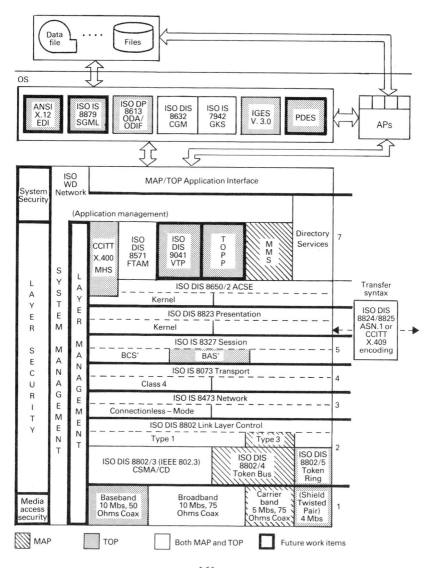

# Appendix 3

# Relevant MAP Organisations

**ISO**
International Organisation of Standardisation
Central Secretariat
1 Rue de Varembe
CH-1211
Genève
Switzerland

**MAP**
European MAP Users Group
Building 30
Cranfield Institute of Technology
Cranfield
Bedfordshire
MK43 0AL
England

General Motors Corporation
Manufacturing Engineering and Development
Advanced Product and Manufacturing Engineering Staff
(APMES)
APMES A/MD-39
GM Technical Center
Warren
MI 48090-9040
USA

Society of Manufacturing Engineers
One SME Drive
PO Box 930
Dearborn
Michigan
48121
USA

**Other Organisations**
British Standards Institution
2 Park Street
London
W1A 2BS
England

CCITT
International Telecommunication Union
Place des Nations
CH-1211
Genève 20
Switzerland

IEEE Standards Office
345 East 47th Street
New York
NY 10017
USA

National Bureau of Standards
Building 225
Room B218
Caitherburg MD 20899
USA

# Index